D1174661

An Introduction to the Philosophy of Time and Space

Studies in PHILOSOPHY

CONSULTING EDITOR: V. C. CHAPPELL
The University of Chicago

BAS. C. VAN FRAASSEN

An Introduction to the Philosophy of Time and Space

RANDOM HOUSE NEW YORK

Acknowledgment is made to the following publishers for permission to reprint excerpts from:

Tractatus Logico-Philosophicus by L. Wittgenstein, translated by D. F. Pears and B. F. McGuinness. Reprinted by permission of Routledge & Kegan Paul Ltd. and Humanities Press.

Aristotle's Physics, translated by R. Hope. Reprinted by permission of the University of Nebraska Press.

The Leibniz-Clarke Correspondence, edited by H. G. Alexander. Reprinted by permission of the Manchester University Press.

Critique of Pure Reason by I. Kant, translated by N. K. Smith. Reprinted by permission of St. Martin's Press Incorporated.

Leibniz Selections, edited by P. P. Wiener. Reprinted by permission of Charles Scribner's Sons.

BD
632
.V27

Library of Congress Catalog Card Number:
70–92829

Manufactured in the United States of America.
Composition by Westcott & Thomson, Inc.,
Philadelphia
Printed and Bound by Halliday Lithograph Corp.,
Hanover, Mass.

Typography by Saul Schnurman

First Printing

To Judy

Preface

This book is based primarily on my lectures in an undergraduate philosophy course on time and space, which I taught at Yale University from 1966 to 1968. Because undergraduate philosophy of science courses are generally intended for philosophy students and science students, it did not seem suitable to require an extensive background in either field. It is hoped that the book will itself provide the philosophy student with some elements of physics and the science student with some elements of philosophy. In addition, the following sections, which deal with slightly more advanced material, may be omitted without essential loss of continuity: Chapter III, Sections 1d, 3b; Chapter IV, Sections 2c-d, 4; Chapter V, Sections 2c, 4, 5; and Chapter VI, Section 5. The remainder assumes only a familiarity with some of the basic concepts of high-school mathematics.

Although this book is therefore quite elementary,

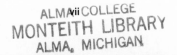

I hope that it will also prove interesting to my colleagues in philosophy. First, it provides an introduction to the highly significant work on time and
space by Hans Reichenbach, Adolf Grünbaum,
and other contemporary philosophers of science.
Second, I have attempted to strike a balance between historical illustration and logical analysis.
In the historical accounts it was my intention to
reconstruct positions and explore their inherent
possibilities, rather than to bare their vagueness
and ambiguities. Although such an attempt is of
little value to the historical scholar, it may be of
interest to the student of metaphysics. In the logical analysis I have used concepts of contemporary
logical theory without using its technical resources;
at present, the notions of possible worlds, logical
spaces, presuppositions (of questions and of definitions), and counterfactual conditionals are of particular logical interest. Chapter VI is based on my
doctoral dissertation on the foundations of the
causal theory of time and deals with subjects of
current research in philosophy of science.

It may seem in order here to make some remarks
on the question of the philosophical point of view.
The traditional view may be summarized as: the
theory of time and space is part of natural philosophy, and this is in turn part of ontology; hence,
the subject can be approached only on the basis of
a specific ontology. First the Critical Philosophy
and then positivism and phenomenology attempted
to discredit this neat scheme of philosophical pri-
orities. But in each of these movements the anti-
metaphysical tendencies proved more lively than
hardy, and in each case we can discern a return to
ontology. Indeed, some very interesting contemporary studies in our subject have a definite ontological point of view.

Nevertheless, I do not think that it is necessary to begin with specific ontological commitments. In my opinion, the philosophy of science gains its central importance in philosophy by providing, at least ideally, a common ground or meeting place for all the major philosophical schools. The physical world picture has an importance for which every philosophy worthy of respect must account. And what the world disclosed by physics is like, is independent of its ontological status. Perhaps it is to be accorded independent reality; perhaps it has only intentional inexistence in the perspectives of the individual monads; perhaps it is best characterized as an intentional correlate of the scientific orientation. In large areas of philosophy of science our concerns are independent of these questions, and our ontological commitments may be "bracketed." And were it not for these neutral areas, areas of common problems, how would fruitful contact between the different philosophical traditions be possible?

Finally, I should like to acknowledge gratefully my great debt to Professor Adolf Grünbaum of the University of Pittsburgh, who directed my doctoral dissertation, and whose own work in this area has been my main inspiration. I would not be a genuine student of his had I not departed from his teachings or his concerns at some points; I expect, however, that any inadequacies of this book will be traceable to such departures.

There are many others to whom I am indebted for reading parts of the manuscript, for helpful comments, or for stimulating conversations on related subjects, and I would like to mention especially Professors R. Fogelin, Yale University; A. Janis, University of Pittsburgh; K. Lambert, University of California at Irvine; S. Luckenbach,

San Fernando Valley State College; W. Salmon,
Indiana University; W. Sellars, University of Pitts-
burgh; R. Stalnaker, University of Illinois; R.
Thomason, Yale University; and my students
J. Hines and P. Kuekes.

Contents

An Introduction
to the
Philosophy
of Time
and Space

Chapter I

Basic Issues in the Philosophy of Time and Space

In this chapter we shall formulate the basic objectives for the philosophical theory of time and space: the most important subjects that must be discussed and the major questions that must be answered.

1. Relations and Order

To say that things happen in time means in part that they happen in a certain order. To say that things are located in space implies that they have a certain position vis-à-vis each other. The following statements all refer to temporal and spatial relations:

(1) The abdication occurred between the two world wars.
(2) The Napoleonic Wars were followed by a period of relative calm.

(3) Belgium is east of England and north of France.

(4) The table stands between the chair and the window.

With respect to time, some of the basic relations are *simultaneous, before,* and *between.* Whether this list is essentially complete, or perhaps redundant in some respects, are questions that we shall not try to answer at this point. (The answers may seem obvious to the reader now, but this impression may change as we follow the history of the problem.) At least, a theory of time must give an account of these relations and thus explicate such common assertions as (1) and (2).

With respect to space, it is not easy even to make a plausible preliminary list of basic relations. It is hard to believe that such relations as *north of* and *east of*—though they are clearly spatial relations—can be in any way basic to the subject. For these relations concern entities on the earth primarily; we may say that Polaris is north of any point on earth, because a sighting of Polaris indicates the northerly direction. But this seems already to some extent an analogical extension of the term "north," and it certainly would not make obvious sense to ask whether Polaris is also north of the sun or of the star Alpha Centauri. Moreover, is Asia Minor east or west of North America? The relation *between* of example (4), however, is not subject to these restrictions and ambiguities. Thus, a theory of space must at least give an account of the spatial *betweenness* relation.

Now, relations give rise to order. We may illustrate this intimate connection between relation and order with a simple example. Suppose that to the question "In what order do you rank the most famous ancient generals?" the answer given is, "I rank Hannibal first, Alexander the Great second, and Leonidas third." This ordering may equally be expressed in terms of the relation *higher than:* the answer might equivalently have been formulated, "I rank no one higher than Hannibal, only Hannibal higher than Alexander, and only Hannibal and Alexander higher than Leonidas."

Similarly, the temporal relations give rise to a temporal order and the spatial relations to a spatial order. Of the two orders, the latter is by far the more complex. Let us assume for a moment that *between* is indeed a basic relation for both time and space. Then we find nevertheless that the order to which temporal betweenness gives rise is much simpler than the order determined by the spatial betweenness relation. To mention the most obvious case: if *X*, *Y*, and *Z* are in time, but not simultaneous, then one of the three is between the other two; it is not true, however, that if *X*, *Y*, and *Z* are in space, though not in the same place, then one of them is between the other two. The reader may recognize this point in the form of the statement "Space is three-dimensional, but time is only one-dimensional." What exactly is meant by *dimension*, however, and how it is related to the complexity of the *order*, and how both these concepts are related to *relation*, constitute a basic problem for the theory of time and space.

2. The Use of Coordinates

Our example of someone ranking Hannibal, Alexander, and Leonidas with respect to military genius also illustrates the subject of *coordinates*. The person who made this statement wished to convey that in his opinion Hannibal ranked higher than the other two generals and Alexander higher than Leonidas—that is, he wished to describe certain relationships that, according to him, obtained among these three. To do so simply and perspicuously, he assigned them numbers: 1 to Hannibal, 2 to Alexander, 3 to Leonidas. This is an elementary use of *coordinates* to describe certain relationships.

How does the assignment of these numbers constitute an assertion that certain relations hold? This is possible because there is a relation among the natural numbers that has the same formal character as the relation *is a better general than* or *ranks in my opinion higher than*. This is the relation *is less than* or *comes before*. One comes before any other natural number; hence, one is assigned to the general, who is ranked higher than any other ancient general. Two is a number such that only one comes before it—hence, two is assigned to the general who ranks next highest.

To put it most generally, coordinates are assigned to entities in such a way that the mathematical relations among the coordinates reflect those relations among the entities that we mean to describe.

And here we find that the kind of order generated by these relations determines what can serve as coordinates. In the case of time, real numbers can apparently serve as time coordinates. In the case of space, however, we need *triples* of real numbers. And this need is again connected with the common assertion that temporal order is a one-dimensional order, spatial order a three-dimensional order. So *relational structure, order, dimension,* and *coordinate system* form a family of closely related subjects, which we must understand if we are to arrive at a coherent account of time and space.

3. Magnitude and Metric

When we say that Boyle was born in 1627, Galileo died in 1642, and Leibniz was born in 1646, we have conveyed the following information about temporal order:

(1) Boyle was born before Galileo died.
(2) Galileo died before Leibniz was born.
(3) Boyle was born before Leibniz was born.

But we have also conveyed information about *temporal magnitude* (duration):

Approximately four times as much time elapsed between the birth of Boyle and the death of Galileo as elapsed between the death of Galileo and the birth of Leibniz.

How much time elapsed between certain pairs of events is not a question of order at all. Yet the time elapsed can also be reflected in the choice of coordinates—as indeed it is in the way we commonly date events. Had we assigned the dates 1627, 1641, and 1642 to the birth of Boyle, the death of Galileo, and the birth of Leibniz, respectively, we would still have conveyed the correct information contained in statements (1), (2), and (3). But we would have conveyed false information about the magnitudes of the two time intervals.

How is information about temporal magnitude conveyed by an assignment of coordinates? In the case of dates, we use the definition

(4) The amount of time elapsed between two events is the *numerical difference* between their dates (time coordinates).

By that definition, and with respect to the time reckoning in terms of years, the assignment of the dates 1627, 1642, and 1646 gives the correct information, and the other assignment does not. But in principle we could use a definition other than (4), in which case we would have to assign dates in a different way if we wish to retain our usual time reckoning.

Definition (4) is called a definition of the *metric* for our system of time coordinates. The definition of time metric can have this simple form because the time coordinates are just real numbers. In the case of space, where each point is assigned a triple of real numbers, the definition of metric is more complex. (Thus, in plane Euclidean geometry taught in high school, in which the points are just assigned couples (x, y), the distance between two points (x, y) and (x', y') is given as $\sqrt{(x - x')^2 + (y - y')^2}$.) To sum up, an assignment of coordinates can reflect relations of magnitude (distance or duration) as well as order, and the question how this is done is the question of *metric*.

4. The Status of the Entity

The words "time" and "space" are both *singular terms*. This is simply a grammatical point about how these words can appear in a sentence. In particular, it means that they can appear as the subject of a singular verb. Thus, the following sentences are both grammatical:

(1) Space is infinite.
(2) The ocean is infinite.

The paradigm use of singular terms is to refer to specific things.

For example. "Paris," "the Atlantic Ocean," and "the man next door" are all singular terms and refer to specific things. Other singular terms such as "heaven" and "hell" were at least intended to refer to entities, approximately in the way that "Greenland" and "America" do. This raises the questions whether "space" and "time" also refer, or are intended to refer, to certain entities, and if so, what kind of entities these are.

These questions take a less academic form when we phrase them somewhat differently. Instead of asking "Is there something to which the word 'heaven' refers?" we could equally well ask "Does heaven exist?" Thus, the questions we have raised about the words "time" and "space" are readily re-phrased as questions about time and space: "Does time exist?" "Does space exist?" "What kind of entity is time?" "What is space?"

This kind of question has a rather unfortunate career in the history of philosophy. Too often the reaction has been: we cannot talk about what does not exist; hence, anything we can talk about, does exist. The question "What is glory?" pre-supposes that there is such a thing as glory; since the question is perfectly meaningful, we must simply take it as our task to explain what kind of thing glory is—and to accept as fact that there is such a thing.

This is exactly the sort of reaction that leads to bloated on-tologies, countenancing various kinds of unreal things as well as real things.[1] But it is not a necessary reaction. For example, the question "What is Pegasus?" has the true answer "A myth-ical flying horse," and neither the meaningfulness of the ques-tion nor the truth of the answer presupposes that Pegasus exists. This is only one kind of example to show that we may well desire to have a correct and adequate account of some-thing that does not exist. Another example is provided by events that did not happen. Consider such a question as "What prevented the explosion?" This question presupposes that the explosion did not occur (just as the question "Have you stopped beating your wife?" presupposes that the person addressed has been beating his wife). Thus, if the question is not mistaken, the term "the explosion" does not have a refer-ent. A final example is provided by the philosophy of religion: we do not believe that Zeus exists, yet we agree that it is true that the ancient Greeks worshipped Zeus, and we may desire a philosophical explication of what is meant by this.

The history of philosophy also provides many examples of positions implying that certain subjects of discourse do not exist. The best known of these is the position, recurrent throughout the development of British empiricism, that no abstract term has a referent. But this view has also always had its opponents, who argue with equal force that abstract entities do exist. In the present century this debate has been most vigorous in the philosophy of mathematics, where the question at issue is whether there exist mathematical objects (as well as physical objects).

The same questions of existence also arise with respect to time and space. In view of the above, we may consider as not a priori absurd the view that time and space do not exist, as well as the view that they do exist. In conclusion we shall briefly consider the kinds of questions that arise for proponents of either view.

First, if it is denied that time exists, for example, this cannot be taken to imply that discourse which employs temporal locutions is meaningless. Whether or not the word "time" has a referent, the sentence

(3) Newton was born after Francis Bacon's death.

is true. And whatever the philosopher's view on the existence of time, he must provide us with an account of what is meant by the use of these temporal terms—that is, we still require an account of temporal relations, of time order, of duration, and of time metric.

Second, if it is held that there is an entity denoted by the word "time," the question what kind of thing it is arises. This question clearly does not arise if it is denied that "time" refers to any thing. But when this is not denied, we may ask whether time is a physical entity or a mathematical object or perhaps some other kind of entity. And this is a question in addition to all the above questions about temporal order and metric.

Finally, we are engaged in philosophy of science, not in metaphysics. Hence, we shall not encumber the discussion of whether time, or space, exists with the further question whether mathematical objects, or other abstract entities exist. Thus, if someone who holds that time exists answers, in addition, that it is an abstract entity, we shall count his answer as prima facie acceptable (though this answer will in turn raise other questions). This position will not, I think, make the discussion useless to those who hold that there are no abstract entities. After all, they are of the opinion that whatever can be said in the terms of their opponents and is somehow significant can also be said in their terms. Nor does this "bracketing" of our ontological commitments provide the question whether, for example, time exists with a trivial answer. For certainly this bracketing will not affect such similar questions about the world studied by physics as whether electrons or unicorns or force fields exist.

Chapter II

The Problems
of the
Theory of Time:
Aristotle
to Kant

In this chapter and the next we shall examine the development of the theory of time before the advent of the theory of relativity. The historical divisions that we make for purposes of exposition are not exact; for example, in this chapter we shall discuss work done in the nineteenth century by the French philosopher Georges Lechalas.

1. Change and Duration:
   The Aristotelian Theory

In Book Delta of the *Physics,* Aristotle develops his theory of what time is and attempts to show its adequacy.[1] In his account, a major role is played by the notions of change, movement, and process. Hence, we shall begin with an exposition of some features of Aristotle's theory of change and then turn to his account of time.

a. Change and Process

Aristotle's definition of movement can be found in Book Gamma of the *Physics*. But the definition is formulated in terms of his theory of act and potency, and bears little relation to modern discussions of the subject. The description of the kinds of change in Book Epsilon is of more interest.[2]

At the beginning of this description we find a distinction between essential change and accidental change. For our purposes, the first kind of change is the more important, so let us attempt to explain what it is.

A change involves (1) a thing that is changed; (2) an initial condition, from which this thing is changed; and (3) a final condition, to which it is changed. To begin, we must consider what kind of conditions the initial and final conditions are. The change will not be an essential change if these conditions are described in terms of relations of comparison. Thus, if Peter is taller than Paul (initial condition), a change might occur that results in Peter being shorter than Paul. But this kind of change is called accidental change when Peter is taken as the subject of the change, because it would occur as a result of Paul's growing up. Thus, in this situation Paul is the subject of an essential change (an increase in his height), but Peter of an accidental change (a change in how his height compares with Paul's height).

The initial and final conditions must be conditions of the same kind. Thus, a given thing might first be hot and later orange, but we would not say that it had changed from hot to orange (this would be a blatant category mistake). Aristotle gives as his example a musician who turns from his music to taking a walk. In both examples, the initial condition is compatible with the final condition: a thing could be both hot and orange, a musician could play music while walking. For this reason, the second is also a case of accidental change.* Essential changes do not take place between compatible conditions,

---

* I disagree, therefore, with the view that this is an example of accidental change because walking is an "accidental property" of a musician.

but "between contraries or their intermediates and between contradictories."[3]

In other words, the various properties that we may attribute to things are here thought of as divided into *families*. An essential change is a change in a subject from one property to another property in the same family. And the members of a single family are mutually incompatible in the sense that a thing cannot have the property P while it has the property Q, if P and Q belong to the same family. One such family would be the family of colors, another the family of heights, a third the family of positions on a chessboard. Thus, examples of essential change would be a change from white to red, a change from being 5-feet tall to being 6-feet tall, and a change (move) from *K3* to *K4* on a chessboard.

We must also note that the members of a single such family must be of the same degree of determinacy or definiteness. Thus, we do not say that a thing changed from scarlet to red, or from light blue to blue, as opposed to from scarlet to crimson, or from light blue to dark blue, or from blue to red. We may explain this by saying that *blue = (light blue or dark blue)*; —hence, that *blue* and *light blue* do not have the same degree of definiteness.

Similarly, *black* and *not-white* do not belong in the same family; indeed, *not-white* belongs only to the family {*not-white, white*}. Aristotle calls *white* and *not-white,* respectively, a substantive and a nonsubstantive (defining "substantive" as "what is referred to in a positive assertion"[4]). This is the occasion for a further distinction among essential changes—between *generation, destruction,* and *movement* or *process.* A change from a substantive to its contrary nonsubstantive is destruction (as from man to not-man); the converse is generation. But a movement or process is an essential change from one substantive to a contrary substantive (as from white to black).

For the discussion of time, movement or process is of primary importance. The movement may be a change with respect to quality (e.g., color), quantity (e.g., height), or place (also called *local motion*). Today we do not generally use the word "movement" unless we have local motion in mind, but this is not how "movement" is to be understood in this context.

A process has parts, and these parts are ordered in a certain way. This was already implied when we said that a change is from an initial condition to a final condition—and of course the change may involve passage through certain intermediate conditions. An important question for us now is whether this order is to be understood as being simply the temporal order. This is important because in his account of time Aristotle relies on this account of processes and change. Hence, if by "initial condition" we mean "condition that immediately precedes the process in time," it follows that Aristotle has simply taken temporal order for granted. This would not vitiate his theory, because temporal order is not the only subject for a theory of time.

My opinion is that there is indeed no adequate theory of temporal order in the *Physics*. This opinion is in disagreement with the *Commentary* on the *Physics* by St. Thomas Aquinas. Aquinas refers to the following statement in the *Physics:*

> ... we distinguish "before" and "after" primarily in place; and there we distinguish them by their relative position. But movement must also have in it a distinction of "before" and "after" analogously to that in magnitude.... The order of "before" and "after" *which* is in process is, existentially, the process; although, indeed, *what* the distinction between "before" and "after" is differs from [*what*] a process [is].[5]

This passage concerns primarily motion with respect to place, and the point appears to be that places are ordered in a certain way. The order of the parts of the movement would then be the order of the places traversed. At least this seems to be Aquinas' interpretation.[6]

Aquinas' argument is that in the case of local motion, certain places are traversed; for example, a body moving from *A* to *C* via the intermediate position *B*. The parts of this movement correspond to these places; for example, the first part of the movement is the position at *A*. Since spatial relations order the positions *A*, *B*, and *C*, the same relations order the parts of the movement: being at *B* would be a part intermediate to being at *A* and being at *C*.

But this argument does not succeed. First, there is no sense in which one position *A* is before another position *B*, except with respect to a certain point of reference. Thus, New York comes before New Haven for a traveler who starts from Baltimore, but not for one who starts from Boston. Second, a position may be intermediate in the journey without being spatially between the starting point and the end point—as when a traveler goes from Baltimore to Boston by way of Chicago. Finally, Aristotle argues at length that only circular motion can be eternal.[7] But circular motion consists in traversing the same positions again and again; therefore, distinct parts of the same process may here consist in being in the same position. Clearly, then, the parts of the only kind of process that can last forever are not ordered through relations of spatial order.[8]

b. Time

The most influential view of time preceding Aristotle's was Plato's view. According to Aristotle's interpretation, Plato identified time with process, and specifically, with celestial revolution.[9] Aristotle objected to this view on several counts. First, a change or process has a location in space, which time does not. Second, movement is fast or slow, but there is no literal sense in which time is fast or slow. In fact, we define "fast" and "slow" in terms of time: "That is 'fast' in which there is much going on in a short time."[10] Nevertheless, time is not conceptually independent of change. The argument Aristotle uses to establish this is phenomenological: we cannot perceive time as such; we are conscious of the passing of time only through discerning change or movement.[11] But this argument can be restated in terms of information: for example, the information that a cruiser's crew was unusually large gives no information about the duration of its first battle, but the information that it covered a distance of 50 miles during this battle does.

This must, therefore, be our point of departure: time is neither identical with nor entirely independent of movement, and it remains for us to determine the relation between them.[12] The distinction between *before* and *after* is introduced as unproblematic or irreducible and is said to order the parts of a process. These parts, as is well known, exist for Aristotle only potentially, in the sense that they could be marked.[13] Being thus a continuous entity, or more generally an entity having potential *or* actual parts, process has a magnitude or "number:"

> For this is what time is: the number of precessions and successions in process. Thus, time is not a sheer process but is a numerable aspect of it. This is indicated by the fact that, as we discriminate "more" or "less" by number, so we discriminate "more" or "less" movement by time.[14]

The medieval formulation is that time is the measure of motion with respect to before and after. "Measure" is here meant in the sense of "magnitude," or "numerable aspect."[15] Thus, local motion can be measured in various ways: we can measure how far (the magnitude with respect to spatial relations) or for how long (the magnitude with respect to temporal before and after). The latter measure is time.

To the modern reader what is striking is that this account provides a definition not so much of *time* as of *duration*. The temporal relation of *simultaneity* is introduced with no indication that a theory of time should also provide an account of this relation. Yet this relation is essential to Aristotle's defense of his definition of time. He does consider the objection that each process has its own magnitude and that hence if time is defined as an aspect of the magnitude of a process, then each process has its own time.[16] This objection, he says, misconstrues his intention: time is the measure or number not of any particular motion, but of motion in general. Given this explanation, the objection rests on an invalid argument: for each process there is a time during which it takes place; hence, there are as many distinct times as there are distinct processes (i.e., it could then not be true to say that two distinct processes happen during, or at, the same time). The invalidity of this argument is demonstrated by showing that it has the same form as another argument that has a patently true premise and false conclusion: each collection has its own number; hence, there are as many distinct numbers as there are distinct collections (i.e., it could then not be true to say that two collections have the same number). Aristotle's example is a collection of seven dogs and a collection of seven horses: these collections are distinct, each has its number (thus, the number of the collection of dogs in question is seven), but it does not follow that these numbers are distinct.[17]

The two collections have the same number because a certain relation obtains between them, namely, a one-to-one correspondence. Similarly, the times of two distinct processes may be the same time, namely, when they are simultaneous. But this relation of simultaneity, a relation of temporal order, is used in the account of what time is. Hence, Aristotle's theory of time is basically a theory of duration.

2. Time and the Possibility of Creation

a. *Aristotle and Aquinas on the Eternity of Motion*

Aristotle had a number of arguments to show that the world, and motion, have no beginning and shall have no end. For our purposes, the most important of these is the following:

> We may here interject the question: how, when there is no time, can there be any "before" and "after"; or how, when there is nothing going on, can there be time? Since time is a number belonging to a process . . . then, if there always is time, movement must be eternal also. . . .
>
> Plato alone presents time as generated; time, he maintains, is coeval with the heavens which, according to him, have had an origin. But if time can neither be nor be conceived without a present, and the present is a sort of "mean" in the sense of being at once the starting-point of the future and the end-point of the past, then there must always be time. . . . Accordingly, if time as an aspect of movement is eternal, it is evident that movement must be eternal also.[18]

Since the argument is moderately complex, let us disentangle the threads. Its basic strategy is to argue that time *cannot* have a beginning, but if motion had a beginning, then so would time.

If both assertions are correct, it follows that motion cannot have a beginning. (The argument applies *mutatis mutandis* to the possibility of an end to motion.)

The argument that time cannot have a beginning has as its premise that a beginning to time is inconceivable. For the moment you refer to an instant, a time *t*, you conceive of a *before* and an *after,* a time before *t* and a time after *t*. Hence, you cannot conceive of a first instant, a time *t* such that there is no time before *t*. But what is inconceivable is impossible; hence, time cannot have a beginning.

Let us not stop here to evaluate this argument, but continue the analysis. The second argument—if motion has a beginning so does time—relies entirely on the Aristotelian theory of time. If time is but a numerable aspect of movement, then time is not something that can exist independently of movement. If this is correct, then it makes no sense to speak of time during which there is no movement. What of the possibility, which at first sight seems so easy to conceive, that all motion should cease, say, for one hour? This, according to Aristotle makes no sense, for an hour is 1/24 of a day and a day is the duration of one journey of the sun around the earth (leaving out astronomical niceties). Thus, it is the motion of the sun that marks the period of one day, and a period of one hour is marked by 1/24 part of that motion. Were only the sun's motion to stop, other motions would mark time periods. Thus, the minute hand of a clock normally has twenty-four revolutions during one day. And if some day all minute hands on clocks (electrical, spring, pendulum, and so on) were to have twenty-five revolutions, we might reasonably believe that the sun had been made to stand still in the heavens for one hour. But if not merely the sun's motion, but *all* change ceased, time would not be marked in any way, and no facts about the physical world would be evidence of the passage of time.

Nevertheless, one might say, we can conceive of this happening, and we can conceive that time would pass in this case. For in principle, we need neither clocks nor any other movement to show that time is passing. We can tell that the sun is standing still for a while by noting that its relative position with respect to the horizon does not change for a while. But here Aristotle argues that then we tell time by the progression of thoughts and feelings in ourselves—were there no change in these either (as in deep sleep), this subjective index would not indicate that time had passed either.[19] Were all change to cease, time should be no more.

For later philosophers, these arguments presented a challenge to the doctrine of creation. If the world was created by God, does it not follow that movement does have a beginning? (They were certainly not inclined to remove the difficulty by saying that God is subject to constant change, without beginning and without end.) We find, accordingly, that neither of the arguments above remained unchallenged in the history of philosophy. Aquinas considered the first inconclusive, but did accept that time does not exist independently of movement. Newton, on the other hand, rejected the second argument and thereby the entire Aristotelian theory of time.

Aquinas' position is unequivocally that movement has a beginning and that this is also the beginning of time. Thus, time has a first instant, an instant before which there are no instants. What then of Aristotle's argument that we cannot conceive of an instant without at once thinking of time before that instant? This Aquinas grants without qualification. But, he argues, this does not entail that there *is* time before the instant in question—that is, he rejects the inference from "That is how we cannot but conceive of it" to "That is how it must be"; the time may exist in the imagination only.[20] In other words, Aquinas solves the problem by positing a distinction between *real time* and *imaginary time*. Any necessity concerning how we *think* of time will be reflected in the structure of this imaginary time (in particular, it can have no beginning or end), whereas the structure of real time will depend on the structure of world history.

But just what are we to think of this imaginary time? What connection does it have with real time? What relation does it bear to movement? If time is a numerable aspect of movement and imaginary time is not, then for what reason is it called "time"? To put it more strongly, Aquinas has accepted and even defended Aristotle's account of time, up to this point where a crucial difficulty appears. At this juncture, he says: There is, besides the time of which Aristotle gives a correct account, also *imaginary time* to which that account does not apply. (Rather like: There is, besides those facts about combustion of which the phlogiston theory gives an entirely correct account, also an aspect of combustion to which the phlogiston theory does not apply.) And although Aquinas has a theory of real time (namely, Aristotle's) he provides no theory of this other kind of time.

This may be a less than charitable reaction to Aquinas' solution. It is a fact, however, that this solution did not close the subject, and the problem played a central role in the development of the theory of time in modern philosophy. Before we look at the issue, however, we must take a brief look at the rather drastic transition from the medieval to the modern temper.

b. The Role of the Theory of Time in Modern Philosophy

In the Middle Ages, Aristotle's philosophy was systematized; its natural philosophy was a part of its metaphysics, its theory of time a part of its natural philosophy. Toward the end of the Middle Ages, and during the Renaissance, this grand philosophical system began to fragment and dissolve. Yet (and this is today a commonplace remark) the beginnings of modern philosophy and science were very strongly indebted to the medieval schools. The theory of time developed by the Cartesians, for instance, was very close to the theory of time of the medieval Aristotelians. But the place of the theory of time in Descartes' philosophy was very different from its place in medieval philosophy.

For the Scholastics, metaphysics deals with substance in general; natural philosophy, or cosmology, is the part that deals with material substances. The primary characteristics of these substances are quantity and quality. There are two kinds of quantity: continuous quantity, or extension, and discrete quantity, or number. Continuous quantity is also of two kinds: permanent and successive; spatial extension belongs to the former, duration to the latter. Both process and the mere endurance of a substance have duration, but endurance cannot be measured except through its relation to change. Thus, time or duration is primarily the measure of change with respect to succession. The theory of time is found exactly here, as part of natural philosophy concerned with successive continuous quantity.

In the Aristotelian-Scholastic system, cosmology is an integral part of its metaphysics; moreover, in this system natural science and natural philosophy are not distinguished. Hence, the account above fixes the place of the theory of time in the Aristotelian philosophy. The gradual disintegration of the Aristotelian tradition was accompanied and followed by strenuous attempts to fashion a new coherent picture of the physical world. The most important result of these attempts was the initial development of modern physics. It is not until the seventeenth century, however, that we find the piecemeal, though important, results organized into systems of natural philosophy that could rival that of the Scholastics. Within these it is already possible to a large extent to distinguish the scientific theories from their philosophical interpretations. The language of the physical theories clearly incorporates temporal locutions; the theory of time has become part of the philosophical interpretation of this language.

In this way, it is possible for the physics of Descartes to be a complete and comprehensive system and for his theory of time to be very brief and relatively uncritical. The situation is similar for Newton and Leibniz. Metaphysics has importance, but as a means of making physics intelligible. This is clear notwithstanding the lip service paid to the older ideal of having physics as a part of metaphysics. Modern natural philosophy is a commentary on modern physics, not a whole of which physics is meant to be a part.

We do not mean to imply, of course, that modern philosophy aims only to be a commentary on physics—although a major reason for its genesis was the need for a new, coherent world picture in harmony with the new physics. Nor do we mean to deny that, at least among the seventeenth-century rationalists, appeal to metaphysical principles was a basic maneuver in the attempt to make physics intelligible. Yet the main point stands: with respect to science, the task that modern philosophers set themselves was to interpret it.

c. Barrow's Argument and Newton's Absolute Time

Sir Isaac Newton's teacher Isaac Barrow considered the problem that had led Aquinas to the distinction between imaginary and real time, but Barrow's reaction was more radical. His solution was to reject entirely the Aristotelian idea that time is an aspect of motion. In his *Geometrical Lectures,* Barrow asks explicitly whether there was time before creation (i.e., whether the instant of creation is, or is not, the first instant). His answer is that "before the world and together with the world (perhaps beyond the world) time was, and is." He immediately goes on to consider the contrary, Aristotelian position:

> But does time not imply motion? Not at all, I reply, as far as its absolute, intrinsic nature is concerned; no more than rest; the quality of time depends on neither essentially; whether things run or stand still, whether we sleep or wake, time flows in its even tenor. Imagine all the stars to have remained fixed from their birth; nothing would have been lost to time; as long would that stillness have endured as has continued the flow of this motion.[21]

So his solution is that time is something independent of motion (unlike Aquinas' real time) and also independent of our thought (unlike Aquinas' imaginary time). Thus, creation simply happens at one of the instants, as decided on by the Creator—just as the Eiffel Tower simply happens to be located in Paris, as decided on by its builders and financers. There is then no need to say that there must be a first instant—something that we cannot conceive. Nor is there difficulty in conceiving that something might have happened before creation, since there are many "empty," "unoccupied" instants that precede the time of creation.

The position that time "flows in its even tenor" independently of the uneven course of world history may thus solve the puzzle concerning the possibility of creation; nevertheless, in some respects it is not a very satisfying position. For it makes time a strange and peculiar entity, whose status will immediately become the subject of philosophical debate. The most obvious positive thing for Barrow to say about time is that it is simply a very important physical entity, like the Milky Way, or, better yet, the system of the fixed stars. But this would, at the least, have to be qualified in important respects: in many ways time certainly is very different from any material body or physical system. At this point (influenced by certain of his contemporaries, e.g., Henry More), Barrow turns to theology. Barrow holds that space and time exist independently of material bodies or physical happenings, but not independently of God. From the viewpoint of natural philosophy, time "does not denote an actual experience, but simply a capacity or possibility of possible existence," whereas from the viewpoint of theology, it represents a superabundance of the divine presence and power.[22] To the modern reader and to any secular philosopher the proposed dichotomy does not help much. When we say to Barrow that if time is not an aspect of motion (nor a construct of the imagination) then it must be some "actual existence" other than any physical process, he answers that from the theological viewpoint, this is so. But if we then admit to being puzzled about what kind of entity this is, he says that from the viewpoint of natural philosophy time is, of course, not any kind of thing at all. From the viewpoint of natural philosophy, this is pure evasion of the issue. Essentially Newton accepted Barrow's theory. In the famous *Scholium* to his *Philosophiae Naturalis Principia Mathematica* he asserts:

> Absolute, true, and mathematical time, of itself, and from its own nature, flows equably without relation to anything external, and by another name is called duration. . . . For times and spaces are, as it were, the places as well of themselves as of all other things. All things are placed in time as to order of succession; and in space as to order of situation.[23]

These and other remarks in the *Scholium* give the impression that Newton takes a much less ambiguous position on the reality of time than Barrow did. Infinite and absolute space and time, independent of anything external, appear to have been posited as entities existing in their own right. Indeed, the theologians of Newton's day were rather disturbed by eternal and immutable entities; Bishop Berkeley attacked them

as "materialistic and atheistic conceptions."[24]   Hastening to
correct this impression, Newton added a *General Scholium* to
the second editon: God is eternal and infinite, and by existing
always and everywhere, "He constitutes duration and space."
But from the viewpoint of natural philosophy time and space
are substantial entities, infinite containers; the theological remarks deny that God has been removed from the scene in favor
of time and space, but do not deny that time and space "denote
actual existences."   And although every seventeenth-century
philosopher was concerned to give his physical world picture a
metaphysical underpinning, it is within the confines of natural
philosophy that this world picture must prove its merits.   From
here on, we shall keep all theological and ontological commitments firmly "bracketed" and consider the disputants' arguments only insofar as they do not burst the bounds of natural
philosophy.

d. Leibniz's Refutation of Barrow's Argument

The contemporary of Newton who most strongly challenged
the theory of absolute time was Gottfried Wilhelm von Leibniz.
This difference became the subject of a lengthy debate by
correspondence between Leibniz and Samuel Clarke.[25] Clarke
was a disciple of Newton, and it is generally acknowledged
that he had Newton's help in drawing up his replies to Leibniz.

In view of the preceding, it does not surprise us to find that
Clarke confronts Leibniz with the following difficulty: If you
do not accept the independent existence of absolute time, then
you cannot hold that the world was created. For if it can be
asserted that God created the world, then it can be asserted
that He could have created it sooner than He actually did. But
what this means is: God could have created the world at a time
prior to the actual time of creation.   And if time is not independent of the existence of the world, then the instant of creation is the first instant.[26]

In his fifth letter, Leibniz answers this challenge.[27]   This
answer is, in my opinion, the conclusive answer to the difficulty; it shows that the dilemma of which Aquinas and Barrow
embraced either horn is not real.   The answer was apparently
too subtle for Clarke, who retorts that Leibniz has landed him-

self in a "plain Contradiction."[28]   The contradiction that
Clarke supposes he sees is this: Leibniz holds that the actual
creation of the world marks the beginning of time and also
grants that the event which is creation could have been temporally preceded by something else.   But this view entails that
something could have happened before time began, which is
absurd.

Leibniz's answer consists in drawing a distinction.   To conceive of something happening before creation can be construed
in two ways, namely, as

(i) to conceive of some event X that it is the first event
and yet is preceded by another event,

or as

(ii) to conceive of an alternative world in which X (which
in this world is the first event) is not the first event.

Now, (i) is indeed an impossibility; but (ii) is perfectly consistent with the view that time begins with the first event.   For in
this alternative world, a different event will mark the beginning
of time.

This answer satisfies all the criteria that must be met to answer the contentions of Barrow, Newton, and Clarke.   First, it
gives a clear sense to our conviction that we can conceive of
something happening before creation.   When we imagine this
possibility, we are imagining an alternative possible world:
one of those possible worlds that happens not to be the real
world.   Second, Leibniz exhibits exactly the contradiction
that was perceived by Barrow and those who followed him;
furthermore, he shows how this contradiction is distinguished
from the view he actually holds.   Finally, he makes it clear
that in the light of these distinctions, it is consistent to hold
that time has a beginning, namely, the time of the beginning
of world history.

But there are still two other questions that we must consider.
The first is a difficulty posed by John Locke, which raises the
question whether Leibniz's concept of possible worlds is adequate.   The second is a difficulty posed by Aristotle and explicitly discussed by Aquinas, namely, that a first instant is

not conceivable; when we think of an instant t, we cannot help but think of time before t.

To discuss the difficulty posed by Locke, we must distinguish between a *conditional assertion of possibility* and a *counterfactual conditional*. Examples of these are, respectively:

    (a) If he had been there, he could have done it.
    (b) If he had been there, he would have done it.

One difference between *could* and *would* is that from (b) we may infer

    (c) If he was there, he did it.

but from (a) we may not infer this.
From (a) we may only infer

    (d) If he was there, he could (may) have done it.

Both (a) and (b) are in some sense about the possible and the impossible, not about the actual. (We may compare (d) with the assertion by Clarke that if God did create the world, then He could have created it earlier.) And Leibniz's ideas about possible worlds give us an explication of conditional assertions of possibility. Thus, according to Leibniz, (a) means

    (e) If there is a possible world in which he was there, then there is a possible world in which he did it.

from which we can infer (by means of the principle that the actual world is a possible world) that

    (f) If he was there in the actual world, then there is a possible world in which he did it.

which is what (d) means. But there is at this point no reason to think that these ideas about possible worlds will help us to explicate counterfactual assertions such as (b).

Locke's *Essay Concerning Human Understanding* appeared in 1690, twenty-five years before the Leibniz-Clarke correspondence. Locke was a great admirer of Newton (as he mentions in the Epistle to the Reader at the beginning of the *Essay*), as were, of course, most of his English contemporaries. It is not surprising, therefore, to find Locke arguing for the independence of time and motion. But he adds something of considerable importance. Writing in 1689, he says that the world is believed to have been created 5639 years before, that is, in the year 3950 B.C. But Locke did not believe the solar system to have been created at the very beginning. "Year," however, means "duration equal to an annual revolution of the sun." It might seem, therefore, that the belief described by Locke is that the world was created a certain number of revolutions of the sun before the creation of the sun. But of course this is not so; rather, what is asserted is that the duration of the world before the creation of the sun *equals* the duration of this number of annual revolutions of the sun.

> The mind having once got such a measure of time as that annual revolution of the sun, can apply that measure to duration wherein itself did not exist. . . .[29]

Now you might think that this could be explained by considering other actual periodic processes that would function as "clocks" in the absence of the sun. But Locke does not mean just that: he means that even if (contrary to fact) some event *X* happened prior to creation *Y*, and then *nothing* happened or existed between *X* and *Y*, there would still be a definite number of years by which *X* precedes *Y*.

> I can imagine that light existed three days before the sun was, or had any motion, barely by thinking that the duration of light before the sun was created was so long as (if the sun had moved then as it doth now) would have been equal to three of its diurnal revolutions. . . .[30]

Here we have the crux of the issue: the truth of the statement "*X* happened five years before *Y*" lies in the truth of the counterfactual conditional "If the sun had existed at the time of *X*, then there would have been five annual revolutions of the sun between the time of *X* and the time of *Y*." This cannot be a truth about possible worlds: there is a possible world in which God creates the sun on the sixth day rather than on the fourth day, and for each number *n* there is a possible world in which the sun actually has *n* annual revolutions between the time of *X* and the time of *Y*.

Leibniz wrote a lengthy work, *New Essays Concerning Human Understanding,* in which he disputes Locke's *Essay,* paragraph by paragraph. When the question is raised how we can meaningfully speak of something happening, e.g., three days before the creation of the sun, Leibniz answers cryptically:

> This vacuum which may be conceived in time, indicates . . . that time . . . [extends] to the possible as well as to the actual.[31]

But in the next chapter he adds something that shows he realized more was at stake:

> . . . if there were a vacuum in time, *i.e.*—a duration without changes, it would be impossible to determine its length. Whence, it comes that . . . you cannot refute the one who would maintain that two worlds, the one of which succeeds the other, touch as to duration, so that the one necessarily begins when the other ends, without the possibility of an interval.[32]

This remark neatly focuses the discussion on the crucial point. For any theory of time in the Aristotelian tradition, according to which time does not exist independently of motion, there can be no such thing as empty time. If nothing happens, no time elapses. And if we try to imagine an interval of time during which nothing happens, we can succeed only by cheating. We can cheat in one of two ways: we can draw an invalid analogy to something picturable (a box with nothing in it, a road with no one on it) or we can imagine ourselves living through the interval (in which case the "clock" is the succession of our thoughts and feelings).

What then of the assertion that darkness was upon the face of the Deep three days before there was a sun? Can this not be true? Leaving out the option that other processes "keep time" instead of the sun, this reduces to a question about the truth of the counterfactual that the sun would have gone three times round the earth had it existed. Can this not be true? Leibniz will have to say No, not in this case. The counterfactual could be true but only if other periodic processes mark out three days in the interval, thereby making the counterfactual true.

And this must be the general direction of Leibniz's answer: a counterfactual can be true, but only because some factual statement is true. Thus, consider "If I were to open my drawer, I should see a bottle of ink." This is true because there *is* a bottle of ink in the drawer (and because I have adequate eyesight, and so on). It would be quite difficult to give a general account of the factual conditions that make counterfactuals true or false. We want to say that what is meant is that in any alternative possible world that is like this one *in the relevant respects* and in which it is the case that I open the drawer, it is also the case that I see an ink bottle. But then it is very difficult to specify what these relevant respects are.[33] In the example above, however, there are *ex hypothesi* no relevant physical conditions such that if they stay the same, and the solar system is also present, then exactly three revolutions of the sun must occur in the indicated interval. In the problem given, there are *ex hypothesi* no factual conditions that would make the counterfactual true (other than facts about absolute time, whose existence is what is in dispute here).

More succinctly, Leibniz need not give an account of how it is possible for there to be empty time, since he can consistently deny that there can be empty time. On the other hand, we must add that another difficult question has been lurking just around the corner. It is the question: Just how is the quantity of elapsed time related to the kind of process that occurs? For example, what if there were no periodic processes, only irregular ones? This kind of question we must postpone, since no real clarity was achieved in this area until the time of Jules Henri Poincaré.

After all these threads have been disentangled, Aristotle's original challenge becomes rather easy to meet. His question was: How can there be a first instant, when we find that we cannot conceive of a first instant? After Leibniz's schooling of our imaginations, we immediately ask what is meant here by "conceiving an instant." What cannot be meant is some fortuitous act of picturing, say, a point on a line. That would at most amount to imagining something that purports to represent time—and the question would then be whether it represents time adequately. But then the only way to conceive of a time *t* is to conceive of it as the time at which something, *X*, happens. And then the assertion that for any *t* we can conceive of a *t'* before *t* amounts to: For any event *X* we can conceive of an event *X'* happening before *X*. But we need not assert that therefore *X* must be preceded by some event *X'*. Instead, Leibniz makes perfect sense of this by saying that we are considering an (alternative) possible world in which *X* is preceded by *X'*.

3. Causation and Time Order

a. Physical Objects and Events

In the *Scholium* to the *Principia* Newton says: "All things are placed in time as to order of succession, and in space as to order of situation."[34] The delightful simplicity of this statement is largely illusory; the use of the blanket term "things" obscures many important distinctions. Some things *exist*, other things *happen*, still other things *obtain*. Thus, the first car I owned, Betsy, existed from 1950, when it was built, until 1962, when it was wrecked. But it is not correct to say that Betsy "happened," or that Betsy "was the case," or that Betsy "obtained." Betsy is a continuant, a *physical object; events,* not physical objects, happen, and *states of affairs* obtain. What happens happens in time, and what exists exists in time; but these two ways of being in time are different.

This was spelled out in detail by Aristotle, who of course used his own theory of time to draw the distinctions.[35] There are two important senses in which something may be said to be in time. The first is that it is measured by time (since time is the measure of movement, *processes* are in time in this first sense). The second is that it is the subject of something which is in time in the first sense—that is, material objects are in time in the second sense, for the subject of a process is such an object. In this sense, something that is at rest is also in time, because a thing cannot properly be said to be at rest unless it is capable of movement. For example, the number two is not in movement; neither is it at rest; there is no sense in which it is in time.

This set of distinctions is adequate as far as it goes, but we must consider events and states of affairs as well as processes.[36] Consider the sentences

(1) *X* was *F* while *Y* was changing from *G* to *H*.
(2) *X* exploded while *Y* was changing from *G* to *H*.

Here the clause "*Y* was changing from *G* to *H*" describes a process. But the clause "*X* was *F*" describes a *state of affairs* (*X* being *F*), or, if you wish, it describes a *state* of *X* (its being *F*). The clause "*X* exploded" describes neither a process nor a state, but an *event* (the explosion of *X*). So what is asserted *is that a certain state* obtained (or that a certain event happened) while the process in question took place. And so temporal relations hold among events, states, states of affairs (situations), and processes.

We can simplify this somewhat. To describe a situation or state of affairs, we would simply describe the states of all the bodies involved in that state of affairs. Hence, it is not really necessary here to discuss states of affairs as well as states. Second, we say that a process occurs when a body changes from being in one state to being in another state. In doing so it will generally pass through some intermediate states. Thus, in a process, a body passes through a series of successive states. The process would be described if we specified this series of states. Therefore, it does not seem necessary either to talk of processes in addition to states.

What we have left now, among those entities which are the subjects of temporal relations, are states and events. What is the difference between these two? Certainly the word "event" connotes suddenness, change, novelty; thus, P. Bridgman writes:

> Examination of usage shows that the "event" is a concept of great generality, applying to many different sorts of physical situation. However, in all its usages it always has a temporal connotation and implies a "happening" of some sort. We are not likely to speak of a book passively resting on a table as an "event"....[37]

If we speak of an event only when a change occurs, it seems plausible to say that an event is a change. Thus, the light is on until 8:08 P.M. and is off thereafter: the going off of the light would be called an event. But this is only one kind of event. Suppose that the light goes off at 8:08 P.M., but stays off only for a second. If events are changes of state, then we would have to say that there are here three states and two events, the events being the change from on to off and the change from off to on. But we are much more likely to report that only one thing happened ("Was it boring to sit in that room for an hour?" "Yes. All that happened was that the light was off for a second.").

So at least some events are very short-lived states. Still, we must consider that some events are changes of state: shall we have to count these among the basic entities related by temporal relations? But a change of state is merely the limiting case of a process; it is a passing through a series of states with only two members. So it is entirely described when we describe this pair of states.[38] This means that the only events that we really have to consider are those that are short-lived states. An interesting reversal of terminology has taken place in the history of the theory of time. The issues that we have just discussed become this clear only in the writings of Bertrand Russell, Alfred North Whitehead, and Hans Reichenbach. And the term which they use for what we have called states and events that are really short-lived states is not "states" but "events." We shall follow this convention, but at times we shall have to point out that these events *are* states of objects.

Let us again consider the question What is in time? Directly in time are those entities which are the basic relata of temporal relations: *events.* Certain aggregates of simultaneous events are called states of affairs, situations, or circumstances: these are also in time. Certain series of successive events are called processes, and these are also in time. The second and third cases concern complex entities that are said to be in time because their constituents are. *Physical objects* are indirectly in time; they are said to be in time because events (which are directly in time) *happen to* physical objects and, in the other terminology, are states of these objects. Thus, my car Betsy existed in time—from 1950 to 1962—because all the events that happened to it (all its states) took place in those years.

We shall now take a closer look at the relations between objects and events, partly to standardize our language a bit more.[39]

A most important attempt to interrelate discourse about objects and discourse about events was made by Reichenbach.[40] He pointed to a parallel between the attribution of some property to an object and the assertion that an event occurred (a state obtained). Thus, the following two sentences are in some sense equivalent:

(3) Elizabeth was crowned.
(4) The coronation of Elizabeth took place.

and so are the following two:

(5) The dynamite exploded.
(6) The explosion of the dynamite occurred.

As we consider more complex sentences, the translation from object language into event language, and vice versa, becomes more complicated too. Thus, determinations of time and place play a rather independent role. Witness the following equivalence:

(7) Elizabeth was crowned at Westminster Abbey in 1952.
(8) The coronation of Elizabeth occurred at Westminster Abbey, in 1952.

Other adverbial modifications introduce further complications, but are not relevant here. Concentrating on simple sentences like (3), we also find, however, that English may have no idiomatic counterpart to generate the event-sentence. Thus, for

(9) The ball was red yesterday.

we only have such contrived event-language equivalents as

(10a) The ball's being red occurred yesterday.
(10b) A case of the ball's being red occurred yesterday.

It is important to notice here that (10b) is a better paraphrase of (9) than (10a). For suppose the ball was painted several times and was red on Tuesday and Thursday but white on Monday, Wednesday, and Friday. Then it would seem most natural to consider the ball's being red on Tuesday and its being red on Thursday as two distinct events. So one case of its being red happened on Tuesday, or was the case on Tuesday, another case on Thursday.

Sometimes English has idiomatic descriptions of events ("coronation," "explosion") and sometimes it does not. Contrived descriptions such as (10a) and (10b), however, can always be manufactured. For this reason, Reichenbach offered the following general pattern:

(11) "(The object) X has (the property) F at time t" is true
      if and only if "A (case of) being F of X occurred at
      time t" is true.

Thus, the general way to describe an event is to say that it is a case of X being F (supplying the relevant object and property terms) and that it happened at a time t (supplying the relevant date).

In addition to this we shall also observe the following terminology:

(12) A given event Y is a case of X's being F if and only if
      Y *involves* X and Y *involves F.*

This formulation is derived from the terminology according to which a person or a car may be said to be involved in a crash or an accident. It is, of course, contrived to extend the terminology in this way, but the extension has many advantages. It is, in general, simpler to say that an event involves a given property than to say that it is a case of something or other's having that property. It also gives a simple definition to an important relation among events: *genidentity*. Two events are genidentical if they happen to the same object, if they belong to the history of one and the same object.

(13) Events X and Y are *genidentical* if and only if there is
an object Z such that X involves Z and Y involves Z.

The history of this object Z is then the aggregate of all the
events in which it is involved.

There are a number of questions about events that are as yet
unanswered. For example, could there be events that do not
involve any physical objects? events that involve several objects? events that involve relations among objects? Are event
language and object language equally rich? Could one theoretically dispense with either kind of language? All are important questions from the point of view of philosophy of
science because of the predominance of both kinds of discourse
in discussions of physics and descriptions of the physical
world. Some of these questions will also become relevant to
our purposes, and we shall then discuss them; but other questions, more peripheral to the philosophy of time and space,
we shall leave unanswered.[41]

b. Leibniz's Causal Theory of Time Order

Leibniz was the first major philosopher to grasp the importance of the subject of order to the theory of time and space.
He saw that the study of order must underlie the study of magnitude or quantity; in this respect he anticipated the direction
of the development of modern mathematics. His own theory
of time and space is basically a theory of temporal and spatial
order.* For this, Clarke charged him with irrelevance, for
"*Space* and *Time* are *Quantities;* which *Situation* and *Order* are
not".[42] It must be granted that Leibniz was not entirely successful in his transition from order to metric, but he correctly
discerned the distinction between them.[43]

Unlike many of his contemporaries, Leibniz was still sym-
pathetic with much in the Aristotelian-Scholastic tradition.
Hence, the question before him was: How can the Aristotelian
account of *duration* be extended or generalized into an account

---

* The main source for this, his essay *The Metaphysical Foundations of Mathematics,* can be understood independently of his general metaphysics. The
interesting aspects of his theory that belong to the latter discipline will not be
discussed here.

of *temporal order?* We may begin by speculating on the train of thought that led Leibniz from Aristotle's account to his own; then we shall restate his position systematically. The former, it is hoped, will give some intuitive motivation for the theory within the philosophical context of Leibniz's work, which a bare reading of his summary exposition will not provide. The latter, on the other hand, will make his theory accessible to critique from a contemporary point of view.

Duration, the quantity of time, is according to Aristotle the measure of motion (in general, change) with respect to before and after. This account presupposes the notions of measure or magnitude, physical change or process, and temporal order. We may rephrase it as

> The temporal magnitude (duration) of a physical change is its magnitude with respect to temporal order.

The question that this raises is: Could the notion of physical change utilized here be used, perhaps in conjunction with certain other concepts, to give a similar account of temporal order? To answer this question, the obvious point of departure is Aristotle's description of physical change. As we pointed out, this account presupposes the notion of a physical substance (or object) subject to various determinations that are divided into families of mutual contraries. This contrariety is itself characterized by Aristotle in temporal terms:

> (1) It is impossible that contrary predicates should belong at the same time to the same thing.[44]

But there are two ways of looking at this characterization. We can think of it as a specification or definition of *contrary predicates* in terms of *necessity* and *simultaneity*. But we can also think of it as an account of why certain predicates never do belong simultaneously to the same thing. Thus, to the question

> (2a) Why is nothing ever red and green (all over) at the same time?

the theory presented summarily in (1) gives the answer

(2b) It is impossible for this to be so, because *red* and *green* are distinct members of a family of contrary predicates.

A possible objection to this answer is that the term "contrary" can only be defined through (1); hence, the answer is circular. But that is a *non sequitur*. We may grant that this is the only way in which "contrary" could be defined here; as long as we *do not* define it, however, there is no circularity. This kind of objection would be made more forcefully by a philosopher who holds that terms *have* some definite meaning; that among all the terms synonymous with a given term, one gives its "real" meaning. The following passage from Kant's *Inaugural Dissertation* appears to involve some such view:

So far is it from being possible that anyone should ever deduce and explain the concept of time by the help of reason, that the very principle of contradiction presupposes it, involving it as a condition. For A and not-A are not incompatible unless they are judged of the same thing together (i.e. in the same time); but when they are judged of a thing successively (i.e. at different times), they may both belong to it. Hence the possibility of changes is thinkable only in time; time is not thinkable through changes, but *vice versa*.[45]

But to this we oppose the view that the terms of a natural language do not have a unique and definite meaning: if one term can be used to define another, then in general, the second can be used to define the first. Any hierarchy of defining terms and terms defined is an artificial construction. Of course, such a hierarchy of definitions may have an important function: it may serve to make sense out of what is meant, it may serve as an *explication*. But there is no term that cannot occur as the subject of an adequate explication, as Kant apparently maintains about the term "time."

Returning to our speculation about Leibniz's train of thought, we notice that one and the same thing may be the subject of contrary properties: such contrary determinations are jointly possible, provided they are *temporally separate*. Their contrariety does not (unlike contradiction) make the existence of one exclude the existence of the other; it separates them, however. And if they are separated, they form a domain of distinct entities, and this domain may be ordered. The domain is world history, and the order, *time*. This is the import of the initial paragraphs of *Metaphysical Foundations of Mathematics*:

> Given the existence of a multiplicity of concrete circumstances which are not mutually exclusive, we designate them as *contemporaneous* or *co-existing*. Hence, we regard the events of past years as not co-existing with those of this year, because they are qualified by incompatible circumstances.
>
>   *Time is the order of non-contemporaneous things.* It is thus the universal order of change in which we ignore the specific kind of changes that have occurred.[46]

Some circumstances are temporally separate because they are actualizations of contrary possibilities; others because they are *qualified* by such intrinsically incompatible circumstances. The use of the concept of *qualification* certainly introduces a new element into the theory into which we must further inquire below. But in the meantime, how are these temporally separate circumstances ordered with respect to each other? Leibniz answers this question with the first attempt at a *causal theory of time:*

> When one of two non-contemporaneous elements contains the ground for the other, the former is regarded as the *antecedent,* and the latter as the *consequent.* My earlier state of existence contains the ground for the existence of the later. And since, because of the connection of all *things,* the earlier state in me also *contains* the earlier state of the other thing, it also contains the ground of the later state of the other thing, and is thereby prior to it.[47]

In other words, according to Leibniz the various circumstances or states of affairs are related to each other as cause to effect, and by definition, the cause is the earlier. After this summary introduction to his theory, we turn to a systematic exposition of it.

In the passages cited above, Leibniz refers to *circumstances.* It is clear that by this he means states of affairs, situations, states, and events. Thus, we shall regard the relations among circumstances that he introduces (mutual exclusion, or *con-*

trariety, and *qualification*) as relations among events. In terms of these primitive notions, he lays down (in effect) the following definition:

(3) Events are *contemporaneous* if and only if they are not contrary and not qualified by contrary events.

By contrary events Leibniz evidently means events that correspond to having contrary properties. In our terminology this means

(4) Events are *contrary* if and only if they involve the same object, but contrary properties.

Both contemporaneity and contrariety are meant to be *symmetric* relations—that is, if X bears the relation to Y, then Y bears the relation to X. According to Leibniz, time is the order of events that are not contemporaneous. To define this order, he introduces an *asymmetric* relation. This is the relation of causality, or (in his terminology) of *containing the ground for*. Using this relation, he can define the relation of temporal precedence:

(5) Event X is *before* event Y if and only if either X contains the ground for Y, or some other event Z that is contemporaneous with X contains the ground for Y.

The theory of time order is given by definitions (3) and (5), which define the two basic temporal relations of contemporaneity (simultaneity) and precedence (succession).

But a theory may be adequate or inadequate, even if it is presented in the form of a set of definitions. In particular we should consider as part of the theory the assertions that contrariety, qualification, and causality are relations among events, the first two symmetric and the third asymmetric.

We must now consider two kinds of questions about the theory. The first kind of question arises if we take the basic notions of events, contrariety, and so on, at face value and then ask: Under what assumptions about the world will Leibniz's theory of time order be a correct account? And the second kind of question arises if we refuse to take the basic notions at face value, and we ask for an account of them also. We begin by considering the first question.

Under what conditions is Leibniz's account adequate? Leibniz's aim is to define temporal relations among events in terms of certain other relations. And so he must hold that these other relations obtain precisely in those cases in which we are prepared to say that the respective temporal relations hold. Consider the relation of being temporally separate (noncontemporaneity). At first glance, one might say that surely two events need not be simultaneous, even if they are not contrary, nor need they be respectively simultaneous with contrary events. After all, what has their being simultaneous or not simultaneous to do with their own character, or with the occurrence of other events?

Let us first take a simple case. We have in the history of the world a short interval during which all events are compatible with one another; yet some of the events occur *later* than others. Is this possible? What it entails is that during this interval nothing changes, for change is from some condition to a contrary condition. So the possibility of the described situation presupposes that there can be a lapse of time in the absence of change. And this is exactly contrary to the Aristotelian tradition in the philosophy, which Leibniz attempts to maintain, that time is not independent of change.

But surely change may be periodic; could we not have two states of the world that are separated by some contrary state but are themselves not contrary to each other? Here we may refer to Leibniz's view that the earlier state contains the ground for the latter. So if we have here an *A*-state followed by a *B*-state, followed by an *A*-state, the first *A*-state is such as to cause (or contain the ground for) a subsequent sequence of states (a *B*-state, then an *A*-state, then . . .). In this, the first *A*-state could differ from the second *A*-state.

Suppose, however, that world history is entirely symmetric about these two *A*-states—what then? It must be noticed first of all that our hypothesis is now cosmological and that with respect to cosmological questions it is often not easy to disentangle the empirical element from the logical. Thus, certain cosmological hypotheses may well be possible relative to one philosophical position and absurd or inconsistent relative to another. In the famous debate between Clarke and Leibniz, Clarke asked Leibniz how he could give an account, consistent with the relational theory of time, of the fact that the world could have been created two years before the actual time of creation. Leibniz's answer was that this is not a fact, that the hypothesis is absurd, and that he only has to account for the feeling or impression that it makes sense. The point is, of course, that relative to the theory of absolute time shared by Newton and Clarke, the hypothesis is possible and relative to the relational theory of time it is impossible. But in the case of a cosmological hypothesis one cannot arrange an experimental situation that would decide between these rival views.

Similarly, with respect to the cosmological hypothesis that two states might fail to be contrary and have exactly similar sequences of states preceding and succeeding them, one surmises that it is incompatible with Leibniz's views. But Leibniz did not explicitly consider this hypothesis, so we can only speculate on what he would have said. It does seem reasonable, however, to believe that he would have appealed to the principle (now called *Leibniz's principle* or the *principle of the identity of indiscernibles*) that two distinct entities must be unlike in some respect. A good example of his use of the principle with respect to a cosmological hypothesis is found in his fourth letter to Clarke, in a discussion of whether God could move the whole universe forward.[48] The application of this principle to hypotheses of symmetric or periodic world histories, however, was not made until much later (see Chapter III, Section 1).

Similarly, we may inquire into the presuppositions of the definition of temporal precedence in terms of causality. As we have phrased definition (5), its adequacy presupposes that whatever happens at a given time t has some cause at each preceding time. Stated in the terminology introduced by the definitions, this amounts to: If X and Y are not contemporaneous, then either X is contemporaneous with some cause of Y or Y is contemporaneous with some cause of X. Now a theory is clearly not complete unless it postulates that the presuppositions of its definitions obtain. (We shall call such postulates "postulates of adequacy.") That Leibniz clearly perceived the need for such a postulate of adequacy for definition (5) is suggested by his assertion, in this context, that "the earlier state in me contains also the earlier state of the other thing, [and hence] it also contains the ground of the later state of the other thing, and is thereby prior to it."[49] And he must lay down some such postulate of universal causality to rule out the possibility of states that are not contemporaneous by definition (3), but that his theory fails to define as either before or after one another. The question is: Is this factual supposition warranted? But this question cannot be answered unless we have a clear criterion for the relation of causality. This brings us to the second line of questioning.

The preceding comments are based on a rough understanding of what Leibniz means by "qualifies" and "contains the ground for." These terms are, however, not nearly so clear that we are inclined to maintain this uncritical attitude. We can see that according to Leibniz if one event qualifies another, then they are simultaneous. (Otherwise definition [3] would not make sense.) But what else is meant if we say that X qualifies Y? We can see two possibilities:

(a) X and Y are not to be regarded as independently existing events.
(b) X and Y are mutually independent, but bear to each other a certain relationship, designated as *qualification*.

If (b) is intended, it is hard to see how Leibniz could defend himself against a charge that either "qualifies" is but a new name for simultaneity or he has postulated a new kind of relation whose sole function is to help him avoid postulating absolute time.

On the other hand, if (a) is intended, the notion of qualification must be further explicated. First, what might one have in mind when referring to events that are not mutually independent occurrences? One possibility is that this refers to the view that we may distinguish between total states and partial states and that partial states are not to be counted as distinct events, but either as aspects of total states or as imperfectly described total states. On this view, the phrases "the car's being wet" and "the car's having a momentum p" are but inadequate descriptions of total states of the car; they might, in fact, both refer to the same state of the car (if the car were wet exactly when it had this momentum). Thus, on this view, the two phrases do not refer to distinct events (though they could be said to refer to distinct aspects of events). And then the relation of *qualifying* could suitably be defined as *being aspects of the same total state*. We might here ask for a criterion of what is to count as a total state. For example, can we refer to the total state of a leg of a table, or would any state of one of the legs be but an aspect of a total state of the table? (This question could obviously be posed for physical systems and their components in general.)[50]

Another possibility is that the reference is to what one might call "second-order" events: events that happen to other events, or involve other events. Examples of these would be the observing of an explosion and the photographing of an explosion. Both examples are most naturally understood as referring to human acts: they are *by someone*. The kind of relation that obtains when a person observes, photographs, dislikes . . . something is called an *intentional* relation. Intentionality is clearly not a subject that belongs to natural philosophy, but the question is whether there are not analogous relations in nature. If there are, then we do have cases of events whose occurrence is not logically independent: for example, the observation of an explosion could not have occurred unless an explosion had occurred. There certainly have been philosophies of nature according to which such interdependence does obtain among physical events.

But I think it is also clear that in either case, a great deal of further explication is needed. Within Leibniz's natural philosophy we find neither an explication of the relation of partial to total states nor of second-order events. (Of course, Leibniz probably did not intend to develop a separate natural philosophy, but regarded this as only a part of a comprehensive metaphysical system. To turn to his metaphysics, however, would lead us outside the scope of this inquiry.)

Similarly, Leibniz's use of causal concepts cannot be satisfactory to us today. The modern reader is at once reminded of Hume's thoroughgoing and radical critique of these concepts. We cannot expect Leibniz to answer Hume's questions

a half-century before they were asked. But from a contemporary perspective, the reliance of Leibniz's theory of time
on the rationalist theory of causation can only be regretted.

c. Kant's Analogies and Lechalas' Theory

(i) Some Remarks on Philosophical Method We have already
encountered two paradigm examples of the method of theory
construction in philosophy: Aristotle's construction of a theory
of duration and Leibniz's construction of a theory of time
order. Theory construction, however, is not the only philosophical method.[51] We have also encountered several examples of what we shall call the *phenomenological method*. We are
here concerned not with the phenomenological method as developed in this century by Edmund Husserl and his students
but with instances of the same general approach found much
earlier in the history of philosophy.

The first example of this method that we have seen was
Aristotle's argument that time is not independent of change.
This argument was that we cannot experience a lapse of time
except through an experience of change. (For example, when
Rip Van Winkle awoke, he was not conscious of any major
change and hence did not realize that much time had elapsed
since he last went to sleep.) Aristotle appeals to the reader's
own knowledge of how he experiences the world. He asks the
reader, in effect, to try and imagine how he would experience
duration other than through experiencing change.

When it is admitted that we cannot imagine A (or experiencing A) independently of B (or of experiencing B), it is concluded that the concept of A and the concept of B are also
interdependent. Why is this conclusion warranted? It
amounts to accepting the principle that what we can and cannot imagine are indications of conceptual interconnections—
put more grandiosely, of the structure of our conceptual
framework. And this does not seem unreasonable as long as
we are merely inquiring into our own conceptual framework.
For one can hardly be said to have a concept of X unless one
can imagine X or think about X; conversely, if I can imagine
X and think of X, then *I* have a concept of X. This is still a
very simple-minded presentation of the method. The primary

reference for a more sophisticated discussion is Husserl's work on eidetic abstraction and the method of free variation.[52]   In the analytic tradition this method is discussed primarily in connection with the subject of intension.[53]   Examples of a very naïve and unself-critical use of the method may be found in David Hume's *Treatise of Human Nature*.[54]

The use of any philosophical method, however, must be hedged round with cautions.   There are two misuses of this phenomenological inquiry that we must especially note.   The first is the mistake of unwarranted generalization.   That I cannot conceive something does not mean that it is not conceivable; my imagination may need to be schooled.   Indeed, it is possible that no one today should be able to conceive of a certain possibility and yet that it is conceivable: radical changes may occur in our common conceptual framework. (There is of course an ambiguity in "cannot conceive": it may refer to one's present conceptual framework or may take into account the possibility of conceptual change.)   The second mistake is probably to be credited to the historical influence of the geometrical method.   It consists in conceiving our conceptual framework as itself being a kind of tacit, implicit, or unconscious *deductive theory*.   If the structure of our conceptual framework is like the structure of a deductive theory, then it has a hierarchy of principles and a hierarchy of concepts. The first hierarchy corresponds to the hierarchy of axioms and theorems, and the second corresponds to the hierarchy of primitive terms and defined terms.   If our conceptual framework really has such a hierarchical structure, then the proper object of philosophical inquiry is to lay bare the basic principles and exhibit the basic concepts, which together provide the foundation for our entire world picture.

This conception, bolstered by the paradigm of Euclidean geometry, has had tremendous influence on the development of Western philosophy.   But we can loosen its grip on our thought by taking a further look at the development of mathematics.   It is indeed true that Euclidean geometry has axioms and theorems.   But it is capable of *alternative axiomatizations* —that is, we can choose some of its theorems to serve as new axioms; then the old axioms belong to the new body of theorems.   Any subject presented in axiomatic form can, in principle, be presented in many other axiomatic forms.   Similarly, the hierarchy of defining terms and defined terms is to a large extent relative to our choice. Often, if A is definable in terms of B, then B is definable in terms of A. All these alternative formal presentations are equally adequate. And we can tell that they are equally adequate; hence, our knowledge of the subject presented is essentially independent of the manner of presentation.

This brings us to the second example of this method, which we have encountered: Kant's objection, in his *Inaugural Dissertation,* that time order cannot be defined in terms of the incompatibility of certain states of affairs, because the notion of simultaneity is part of the meaning of this incompatibility. To this we object that simultaneous and mutually incompatible are not conceptually independent, but that this does not establish a hierarchy. It means that either is a candidate for being defined (partly) in terms of the other. Which course of definition we choose will depend on our immediate purpose. Since our present purpose is the explication of the subject of time order, we shall prefer to give a definition of "simultaneous," if we can.

These remarks on method are relevant because we are about to examine another instance of phenomenological inquiry. At least, this is how we shall interpret Kant's section "Analogies of Experience" in his *Critique of Pure Reason.*[55] We shall also see how such an inquiry may provide the philosopher with the raw material for theory construction. For a nineteenth-century French philosopher, Georges Lechalas, chose this as his point of departure for a new theory of time order.

(ii) The Analogies of Experience   Kant's answer to the general question What is the structure of our experience? may be summed up thus: We experience ourselves as perceiving other entities and ourselves together in a world, which has a certain structure. The next question is then: What is the structure of this perceived (phenomenal) world? To this, the *Transcendental Aesthetic* gives the answer space and time—that is, we experience the objects of (outer) perception as being all in space and all in time, as spatially and temporally related to each other. But here we may ask: What does it mean, for example, to say that we perceive things *as* spatially related to each other? Kant's answer here may be summed up as follows: The subject has already a certain conceptual scheme, and he organizes the data of perception within this scheme. What this answer amounts to is explored in the *Transcendental Analytic;* and we shall here look at a small part of the exploration that deals specifically with time, the section titled "Analogies of Experience."[56]

The principle of these Analogies is that objective experience "is possible only through the representation of a necessary connection of perceptions." The perceptions themselves come in almost entirely accidental order, so they could not automatically yield a coherent picture of a world, such as we actually have. Specifically, the analogies deal with time: we perceive events, and events are ordered in time. Since we cannot perceive time itself, the mind needs certain rules whereby it reconstructs this order. And these rules, or principles, whereby the mind organizes what it perceives into a temporal sequence, are the Analogies.

Time has three main aspects, says Kant: duration, succession, and simultaneity (coexistence).

> There will, therefore, be three rules of all relations of appearances in time, and these rules will be prior to all experience, and indeed make it possible. By means of these rules the existence of every appearance can be determined in respect to the unity of time.[57]

What these three rules do, insofar as this is of interest to us for the theory of time, is to relate these temporal concepts to other concepts applying to the physical world: duration to substance, succession to causation, simultaneity to reciprocal interaction.

First, we represent events to ourselves as all ordered in a temporal sequence. But why do we not conceive of them as ordered in several sequences, having no connection with each other at all? Kant's answer is that we conceive of all events as involving objects and that objects endure through change. Thus, a *single* object may be involved in many events, and this is the reason we conceive of these events as all belonging to a single sequence: the history of that object. An object is a continuant, an enduring substance, and the First Analogy says that all change consists in alteration in the determinations of an enduring substance:

> Substances in the [field] of appearances, are the substrata of all determinations of time. If some of these substances could come into being and others cease to be, the one condition of the empirical unity of time would be removed. The appearances would then relate to two different times, and existence would flow in two parallel streams —which is absurd.[58]

The passage just cited does not rule out creation, but it only allows the creation of all substances at once. It rules out the possibility that any object should come into being after creation—on the ground that the states of that object would not belong to the same world history. This is a very implausible point: prima facie, those states would be simultaneous with certain events in the given world history and therefore also belong to the same world history. Suppose, however, that all substances cease to be and other substances whose states are not simultaneous with any states of the former come into being. The way in which we have phrased this supposition suggests that the other substances exist after the former. But closer scrutiny will show that this is not entailed: there is no ground for asserting *any* temporal relation between the states of the former and those of the latter, except nonsimultaneity. So there would be no way of ordering them all together into a single world history. Since we suppose that such an ordering is always possible, this supposition is absurd. But the removal of the absurdity does not require the assertion that there is no coming into being or ceasing to be of substances.

On the other hand, in many passages Kant uses the word "substance" in the singular. So we may also understand it as a "mass-term"; for example, as meaning *matter*. Then we may conclude with him that, within world history, all matter does not cease to be and then come into being again. This does not entail that *some* matter may not be generated or destroyed.

Before going on to the Second Analogy, it may be well to reflect once more on Kant's aim. The world picture to which Kant addresses himself is clearly not just the "manifest image" (as Wilfrid Sellars calls it) formed by us in prescientific reflection. It is the world picture of the physics of his day, which explains why he wishes to deduce that "substance is permanent; its quantum in nature is neither increased nor diminished." This scientific world picture was conceived as being in some sense *necessary;* its principles were not seen merely as accidental truths. For this reason, the seventeenth-century rationalists had attempted to infer some principles of modern physics from basic metaphysical principles. (And in this they followed the Aristotelians, who had attempted to do so for *their* physics.) Kant, on the other hand, attempted to show that the basic principles of modern science correspond to basic features of our conceptual scheme, which determines the structure of any possible experience. It is not easy for us to appreciate how strong a hold classical physics had on those to whom it was contemporary. We are therefore unconvinced that Kant is uncovering the sole conditions under which coherent, objective experience is possible. But we may still agree with Kant about the importance of the concept of *substance* or *enduring physical object* for the characterization of the relational structure of events in time.

The Second Analogy similarly connects succession with causation. Kant feels he has demonstrated that whatever happens must be conceived of as an alteration in the state of a substance. Now he asserts that any such alteration takes place in conformity with the law of cause and effect—the law that everything which happens "presupposes something upon which it follows according to a rule." As Hume's criticism had convinced Kant, this causal connection is not itself perceived, just as time is not itself perceived.

> In other words, the *objective relation* of appearances that follow upon one another is not to be determined through mere perception. In order that this relation be known as determined, the relation between the two states must be so thought that it is thereby determined as necessary which of them must be placed before, and which of them after, and that they cannot be placed in the reverse relation.[59]

This does not seem to add much, for us, to Leibniz's discussion. The further discussion of the concept of causation in this section of the Second Analogy also touches on the subject of the *continuity* of change and causal action, another feature of classical physics that Kant considered conceptually necessary. But from our present point of view, the most original aspects of Kant's discussion of time concern simultaneity.

In the case of the Third Analogy it is instructive to look at Kant's statement in both the first and the second editions of the *Critique of Pure Reason:*

> All substances, so far as they coexist, stand in thoroughgoing community, that is, in mutual interaction.[60]
>
> All substances, insofar as they can be perceived to coexist in space, are in thoroughgoing reciprocity.[61]

In the second edition, more emphasis is placed on how we perceive that certain things (states of affairs) exist simultaneously. Sometimes we perceive both simultaneously, that is, our *perceptions* are simultaneous. That is, of course, not enough for two perceived events to be simultaneous: if we hear a thunderclap and see a bolt of lightning simultaneously, and we also know that the storm is far away, we conclude that the two events were *not* simultaneous. For we know that sound does not travel as fast as light. But if we see two events happen, and we judge them to be in nearly the same place, and the two visual perceptions are simultaneous, we conclude that the events happened simultaneously.

This discussion already shows that regard to causal interaction is central to judgments of simultaneity. (In the case of seeing, Kant says, "The light, which plays between our eye and the celestial bodies, produces a mediate community between us and them, and thereby shows us that they coexist."[62] In the case of hearing, the interaction would be through sound waves.)

But there is also a more complicated case, namely, when we are situated so that we cannot perceive both coexistents at once. Then, if they are brief events, we cannot perceive that they are simultaneous. But if they are objects, we can perceive that they do coexist throughout a time interval.

> Thus I can direct my perception first to the moon and then to the earth, or, conversely, first to the earth and then to the moon; and because the perceptions of these objects can follow each other reciprocally, I say that they are coexistent. Now coexistence is the exis-

tence of the manifold in one and the same time. But time itself cannot be perceived. . . .[63]

The problem is then: Why do I not instead arrive at the judgment that the moon appears when I look in a certain direction and disappears when I turn my eyes to the earth? Kant's answer here is that by organizing our perceptions into a world picture containing moon and earth as enduring, coexisting substances, we are in a position to explain why the perceptions can follow each other reciprocally.

But he wishes to say more here: he wishes to say that we must conceive of the moon and earth as being in reciprocal interaction, for this world picture to be fully coherent. That does not seem to be implied, however. The hypothesis of light waves connecting both the moon and the earth with the perceiver seems to be sufficient to explain his perceptions. But Kant is clearly after something more: he wishes to exhibit a necessary ground for some law such as Newton's law of universal, mutual, gravitational attraction.

Here we move to an argument that was given more emphasis in the first edition and returned to in a footnote at the end of the section.[64] For a collection of substances to form one world and be set in one time, it is necessary that they be in continual interaction. Otherwise, the states of one substance would form one time series and the states of another substance would form another time series, and there would be no objective way of correlating the two series.[65]

The unity of the world-whole, in which all appearances have to be connected, is evidently a mere consequence of the tacitly assumed principle of the community of all substances which are coexistent. . . . And if their connection . . . were not already necessary because of their coexistence, we could not argue from this latter, which is a merely ideal relation, to the former, which is a real relation. We have, however, . . . shown that community is really the ground of the possibility of an empirical knowledge of coexistence, and that the inference, rightly regarded, is simply from this empirical knowledge to community as its condition.[66]

As we have said above, today we cannot see this as an uncovering of necessary conditions of a coherent world picture.

But we can agree that Kant has ferreted out some crucial features of the world picture of classical physics and has correctly drawn attention to their connection with temporal concepts.

(iii) Lechalas' Causal Theory of Time Order

Lechalas took his departure from Kant's "Analogies of Experience" in an attempt to define temporal order by means of the concepts of classical physics.[67] Unlike Kant, he was not concerned with a possible foundation for any coherent physics or with demonstrating that certain features of extant classical physics have a claim to a priori certainty. He was content to use the concepts furnished by physics, rather than to rely on any philosophical framework. This makes his effort all the more important, since the extant sciences provide a kind of "given" for philosophy: for a philosopher, the conceptual framework of the science of his day provides a subject more appropriate for analysis than for criticism. Other philosophical systems, of course, are fair game. (Both these points need to be qualified, but the distinction will be clear.)

We may begin by considering a crucial passage in Lechalas' *Etude sur l'espace et le temps:*

> Concerning the world of material bodies, the principle of mechanical determinism asserts that the state of a system of material points at a given instant is determined by its anterior states and determines its posterior states. For us, this law amounts to the assertion that the states of this system determine each other and that the determining states are called, *by definition,* anterior to the determined states— each state being, of course, at once determining and determined, depending on whether it is considered in relation to one or another of the various states.[68]

Thus, Lechalas makes the following claim: Each state of a mechanical system is determined or caused by other states of that system; also, it determines certain other states. And this relation of determination is such that the states that occur before a given state are exactly those that determine it—and those that it determines are exactly those that come after it. Moreover, this determination is described by the laws of mechanics. Therefore, the temporal succession of the states of a mechanical system is (implicitly) described by these laws.

To make this more plausible, we may look somewhat more closely at classical mechanics. It was found that the motions of bodies of ordinary ("macroscopic") size can be described very accurately if they are regarded as collections of particles. These particles (called "material points" by Lechalas) each have a certain mass, and at each instant, a location, a velocity, and an acceleration. (The velocity may be defined as the rate of change of the location, and the acceleration may be defined as the rate of change of the velocity.) Finally, at each position a given particle may be subject to certain forces (such as gravitational attraction, which is exerted on it by other particles).

The motion of these particles is held to be governed by Newton's laws:

(1) A body continues in a state of rest or uniform motion along a straight line, unless it is subject to a force.
(2) If a force acts on a body, then the body has an acceleration in the direction of that force, and the magnitude of the acceleration is directly proportional to the force and inversely proportional to the mass of the body.
(3) The forces exerted by two bodies on each other are equal in magnitude and opposite in direction, along the line joining their positions.

The first law is also called the *law of inertia,* the second is more familiarly presented as equating force with mass times acceleration, and the last is popularly stated as "for every action there is an equal and opposite reaction."

A mechanical system is a collection of such particles, which exert forces on each other (the internal forces of the system); there may also be external forces on the system. In principle, the specification of these forces and of the positions, masses, and velocities of the component particles may be utilized to describe the trajectory of the body—given only the above laws of motion for the particles. The state of a system at an instant t is to be given through a specification of the states of its component particles at t. If the notion of *state* is here to be such that the laws of motion and the state at t together determine all subsequent states, then the state of a particle must comprise its velocity as well as its mass and position. (Moreover, we must know what forces are operative at each relevant position.)

Returning to Lechalas' theory, we may ask: Suppose that the states of system S_1 are thus temporally ordered; and also the states of system S_2; how are the two temporal sequences to be related to each other? For this we clearly need simultaneity. Following Kant, Lechalas sees physical interaction and, specifically mutual gravitational attraction, as the physical correlate of simultaneity.[69] That is, at any given time t, the body S_1 exerts a gravitational force on the body S_2, similarly, S_2 exerts an (equal but opposite) gravitational force on S_1.

Suppose S_1 is a stone released near the earth, S_2, at a distance d from the center of the earth. Then the earth attracts the stone, and the stone attracts the earth, with an equal force. The acceleration of the stone is calculated by dividing the magnitude of the force by the stone's mass. Similarly, the acceleration of the earth toward the stone is calculated by dividing the same magnitude by the earth's mass. Since the earth's mass is much greater than the stone's mass, the acceleration of the stone will be much greater than that of the earth. As a result, the stone and the earth approach each other. The magnitude of the forces is a function of the distance between them and so will vary during this approach. But at each instant, the force exerted on the stone by the earth *equals* the force exerted on the earth by the stone. Lechalas' aim is to utilize this fact to define a relation of simultaneity between the states of the two systems.

We shall now examine this attempt critically. Before we do, we may note that in this attempt Lechalas' aim was similar to that of Leibniz. In fact, whereas Leibniz was the first to construct a causal theory of time, Lechalas was the first to use the term "causal theory of time." Whether Lechalas' attempt is any more successful than Leibniz's remains to be seen.

The first major objection to Lechalas' theory is that the language of classical mechanics is a thoroughly temporal language. It is full of temporal locutions—as our brief exposition above has already shown. First, we mentioned that to specify the state of a particle, we must give its velocity as well as its position, and we also said that the velocity may be defined as the rate of change of the position. The latter definition would use the notion of time: "rate of change" is the same as "rate of change with time."

In itself, this is not an insuperable obstacle to Lechalas: it means only that he cannot define "velocity" in this manner. But of course, he can take it as an undefined term. There are many terms in mechanics that are defined by means of temporal locutions *in the ordinary development of the theory*. That can be taken to mean simply that Lechalas had in mind an alternative theoretical development of the science of mechanics. In the nineteenth century the idea of such a drastic reformulation of mechanics was not uncommon. For example, the energetists wished to develop a theory in which energy was the basic, undefined concept. Their efforts, however, were not successful and are now all but forgotten; no alternative development of mechanics that does without the use of an explicit time variable exists. This alone is quite a drawback to Lechalas' theory.

Second, let us consider his attempt to define simultaneity. This relation is needed at this point if we wish to specify the state of a complex system; for this would involve the simultaneous states of its component particles. Now there is a mutual gravitational attraction among the individual particles (or individual systems). Can this attraction—the mutuality of instantaneously induced accelerations among these bodies—be reconstrued as a relation among their states?

Lechalas' expositor Henryk Mehlberg is of the opinion that this can be done. He argues that if we wish to find the state of particle Y that is simultaneous with the state E of particle X, then we simply measure the force with which Y attracts X at the moment of the state E. Among the states of Y, the one in which the force by which X attracts Y is equal and opposite to the aforementioned force is simultaneous with E.[70]

But this will not do. First, there is the glaring circularity in the use of the phrase "at the moment of the state E."[71] Second, it is possible for two bodies to attract each other with the same force at different times, namely, if they have the same positions at those times. Third, if there are more than two bodies in the world, the total force on X at a given time is compounded vectorially from the forces exerted on it by all the other bodies. Given the resultant force on X at the time of E, we cannot determine the component force exerted by Y alone, unless we know either the position of Y at that time or the positions of all the other bodies at that time.

In other words, gravitational attraction (classically conceived) cannot be used to correlate the histories of the various gravitating bodies. This is a very important point, for it marks the failure of Lechalas' attempt to characterize simultaneity in terms of the concepts of classical mechanics.

But let us momentarily grant Lechalas the notion of state of a mechanical system. There is still the question In what sense can the laws of mechanics be said to define the temporal order of the states of a given system?

We might first understand this assertion of Lechalas' to mean: mechanics provides a description of certain physical relations that hold among the states and that could be used to define their temporal relations. But if that was Lechalas' intention, it would have been his task to show that the laws of mechanics have a certain "nontemporal core." That is, these laws are stated in temporal language; he would have to show that they entail statements (expressed without the use of temporal locutions) describing these physical relations. But this is not something attempted by Lechalas.

There is, however, another way to understand this assertion. Consider the totality of all states of a given system and consider all the ways in which these states may be arranged in a linear order. For many of these orderings, the laws of mechanics will rule out the possibility that they correspond to the actual temporal order of the states. (For example, the laws rule out discontinuous motion.) The question is: Do the laws rule out *all but one* of these orderings of the states? If so, that one must also be the actual one, and then the temporal order of the states may be defined as their only possible order not ruled out by the laws of mechanics. The second way of understanding Lechalas is to take him to be asserting that only one possible ordering of the states is compatible with the laws of mechanics.*

---

*Since these laws are time-reversible this would at least have to be a betweenness-ordering, instead of a before-after ordering: alternatively, one might perhaps add the second law of thermodynamics (see Chapter III, Section 3).

Lechalas made no attempt to demonstrate that this is so. But more important is the fact that even if this is correct, the result is a rather weak, if not trivial, theory of time order. Certainly, if classical mechanics has this feature, its theoretical achievement is to be admired even more. But could this feature be said, in any sense, to give us an explication of temporal concepts?

In conclusion, we may say that Lechalas saw quite clearly what a theory of time order had to achieve. He also decided, in my opinion rightly, that such a theory ought to utilize the concepts of physics rather than the concepts of any philosophical system. But his attempt failed: the laws of motion cannot define temporal succession, and gravitational attraction, classically conceived, cannot define simultaneity.

Chapter III

The Problems of the Theory of Time: the Nineteenth Century

In this chapter we continue our examination of the development of the theory of time, concentrating on problems which became clear mainly during the nineteenth century. Some of the work discussed, however, was done during the twentieth century, our main criterion being that the problems examined can be understood without reference to the theory of relativity.

1. The Topological Structure of Time

a. Topological Questions

In Section 2 of Chapter II we discussed the questions whether the world could have a beginning (creation) and whether time could have a beginning. We found that these were not entirely separate questions, at least when the discussion began (in the tradition deriving from Aristotle), and that the main issue became: Are these separate questions, or not? A major position, represented by Barrow and Newton, was that the questions are separate. But the arguments for this position rested on a modal confusion, as was shown by Leibniz.

A question such as whether time has a beginning (or an end) is a *topological* question. This terminology is derived from geometry, where we may distinguish between questions of topological structure and of metric. This distinction is a precise version of the well-worn distinction between quality and quantity. That a line segment is twice as long as another line segment, and that two triangles are congruent, are propositions concerning metric. Even the proposition that two triangles are similar concerns the metric, for this proposition concerns the equality of certain angles; and this equality is an equality of magnitude.

What constitutes a topological feature, then? A topological feature is one that is preserved by a one-to-one continuous transformation. To put it in visual terms, it is a feature that is preserved under any deformation (stretching, twisting, smoothing out) that does not weld or tear the figure or break connections. In the case of a triangle, the obvious topological feature is that the triangle encloses a certain area: if point *A* is inside the triangle and point *B* is outside the triangle (in the same plane), then any line joining *A* and *B* (on that plane) must cut some side of the triangle. You could stretch the plane, deforming the triangle into a circle or a half-moon or a square, but the boundary would always be between *A* and *B*.

Leibniz and Kant, as well as many other writers, stated explicitly that the topological structure of time is that of the real line. That means that time has no beginning or end and that it has only one dimension (unlike space, which has three dimensions). A circle also has those properties, however. Yet a line and a circle are very different even from a topological point of view: in geometric terminology, a line is an open curve and a circle is a closed curve. But both are unbounded: they have no beginning or end.

The subject of Section 2 of Chapter II may therefore be characterized as follows: Is there a connection between the topological structure of time and the topological structure of world history? The specific point debated was whether, if world history is bounded on one end, then time is bounded on one end (where "bounded on one end" is neutral between "has a beginning" and "has an end"). The issue between the absolute and the relational theory of time is clearly the more general question. If time flows on in its own, even tenor, independent of the physical world (to use the flowery language of the English physicists), then its topological structure is independent of world history. But if temporal relations are somehow constituted by physical relations, this is not so.

The question of creation is a rather obvious one, given the Judeo-Christian theological tradition. In the more secular spirit of the eighteenth and nineteenth centuries, the unbounded time assumed by Newton did not need to expect much opposition based on the theological doctrine of creation. But given that time is unbounded, there is still the question Is it topologically open or closed? Does time have the topological structure of the real line or of a circle?

It might be thought that physics could settle this question readily. In classical physics, one certainly takes real numbers to be the values of the time variable. But this does not rule out that the real numbers are not the only admissible values. Sometimes the physicist says: let t vary from minus infinity to plus infinity. This means: let t take all real numbers as values. But this does not rule out that the physicist is still concerned only with a proper part of time. If he is, this could hardly be expected to affect the experimental success of his science, which had such a profound effect on modern philosophy. For any practical application of his theory would certainly concern only a small stretch of time.

If we admit that other values for the time variable (besides real numbers) are not ruled out, then we must admit that time may be topologically closed. For a line may be conceived of as a part of a circle, namely, as a circle with one point missing. If the reader is not familiar with this subject, he may have some objections. First, we must emphasize that we are speaking from a topological point of view. If you take one point out of a circle, you do not produce a straight line, but being straight or crooked or curved is not a topological property. Second, the line produced is finite if the circle was finite, but that kind of finitude (having a finite magnitude) is not a topological property either. Finally, if one imagines the point removed from the circle, it may at first seem that what is produced is a line segment bounded on both ends. This is not so; the line so produced does not have end points. We may illustrate this by referring to what happens if we remove the end points from a line segment that does have them. Suppose each point is given a real number, in the usual way, and suppose the line segment corresponds to the interval [0,1]. This is a closed interval; taking away the end points 0 and 1 produces the open interval (0,1). This interval does not have end points. Similarly, if we had removed the point 1/2, we would have produced two disjoint intervals [0,1/2) and (1/2,1], which are each bounded on only one end.

But what of time order? If we take the before-after relation for granted and make some plausible assumptions, then time cannot be topologically closed. These assumptions are:

(1) Of any two events, either one is before the other or they are simultaneous.
(2) If *A* is before *B* and *B* is before *C*, then *A* is before *C*.
(3) No event is before itself.

If we then represent instants by points on a circle, in the obvious way, we see that all events *are* before themselves (by going all the way around the circle) in contradiction with (3). And surely, principles (1)–(3) hold. But this is not so incontrovertible a point either. For (1) refers to *all* events and says that they are all placed in certain before-after ordering. But any evidence we may have for this will concern only a small part of world history: the part with which we are directly acquainted or, if you wish, the part of which accepted scientific theory now gives a fairly clear picture. But again, this part may not be all. The phenomenological distinction between before and after may be a local rather than a cosmic distinction. (We shall return to this subject in Section 3.) On the other hand, one might hold that principles (1)–(3) follow from the meaning of "before." In that case, one faces the factual question whether world history really has this structure—unless one holds to the absolute theory of time.

b. Nietzsche's Theory of Eternal Recurrence

Granted, then, the possibility that time may be topologically closed, what could ever lead to the conclusion that in fact it is? It is at this point that we must turn to the theory of *eternal recurrence,* the theory that each state of the world recurs infinitely many times. Versions of this hypothesis existed among the pre-Socratics, and the hypothesis was again widely discussed during the nineteenth century. The best-known nineteenth-century proponent of the theory was Friedrich Nietzsche.[1]

As we have stated the theory, it still allows various alternatives; for example:

(1) Each state that occurs has already occurred infinitely many times.
(2) Each state that occurs will thereafter recur infinitely many times.
(3) Both (1) and (2).

Also, we implied nothing about the order of recurrence. Here an especially interesting possibility is given by:

(4) The world process is periodic or cyclical.

What (4) adds is that not only the individual states but a certain *sequence* of states recurs. This is suggested by the doctrine of determinism that we encountered in Lechalas: the nature of a total state of the world uniquely determines the sequence of states that follows it. To distinguish (4) we shall call it a theory of *cyclical recurrence.*

How could one have empirical evidence for such a theory? The situation is not fundamentally different from that for any cosmological theory. If according to our physics, the physical world is ultimately deterministic, and one had evidence for the hypothesis that present conditions are such that this deterministic process will eventually lead to the same state again, one would have evidence for cyclical recurrence.[2]

According to the theory of cyclical recurrence, then, world history consists of a series of cycles, each exactly like the others in all respects. But although this is a perfectly possible hypothesis vis-à-vis the Newtonian, absolute theory of time, it was soon pointed out that it conflicts with Leibniz's point of view. This is brought out by a criticism directed at Nietzsche by H. Bois:

> By means of reasoning analogous to a well-known argument of Leibniz, we may object to Nietzsche: your conception must result in a denial of the reality of this succession of identical worlds, which you have supposed to be infinite. The identical worlds, which according to you succeed each other, are in themselves indiscernible from one another, because they have no intrinsic differences. There will be no way in which these worlds can be distinguished from one another, unless you put a limit to the phenomena and to the worlds of the past, so that, for example, a certain world can be called the first, the next the second, and so on. But if one declares, as you do, that past time is infinite, . . . then each new one, no matter how far back one goes, is preceded by an infinite number of identical worlds, just as it will be followed by an infinite number of worlds in the future. These identical worlds . . . would differ only numerically, *solo numero*. It follows from this that, for our reason, they are reduced to a single one and that the hypothesis of Eternal Recurrence destroys itself.[3]

The argument proceeds by appeal to Leibniz's principle of the identity of indiscernibles and concludes that the theory of eternal cyclical recurrence is inconsistent.[4] Two questions arise here: Is Leibniz's principle to be accepted? and Granted the soundness of the argument, what must the structure of world history be, according to the Leibnizian, when the factual conditions are those that lead the Newtonian to conclude eternal cyclical recurrence?

Leibniz's principle of the identity of indiscernibles states that if entities A and B have all properties in common, then they are identical—that is, then A and B are one and the same entity; the terms "A" and "B" have the same referent. One might understand this in a trivial way: for example, by counting being identical with A as one of the properties. But that is not how the principle is meant: the word "discernible" is to be taken literally. We may best understand the principle and its converse (if A is B, then A has all the properties that B has) as together giving the meaning of the predicate "is identical with." Since their inception both the principle and its converse (which logicians often call *Leibniz's law*) have been attacked by philosophers. This dispute should not be seen as a metaphysical debate; we can best regard it as raising the question whether Leibniz's principles provide us with an adequate explication of the notion of identity.

A common argument against the identity of indiscernibles is that we can easily conceive of a possible world containing two distinct things that are alike in all respects (say, two perfect, black spheres).[5] And surely conceivability implies possibility; therefore, the vaunted principle is not a necessary one. But one must take great care in concluding that something is conceivable. In some sense, I can conceive myself squaring the circle—but that is not possible. In imagining the world containing two spheres that are exactly alike, how do I "see" that they are distinct? Possibly by reflecting that if I were in that world, one sphere would be to my left (I would then call it A) and one would be to my right (which I could then call B). But then the question is: Does this counterfactual assertion express a property of the spheres? If the truth of this counterfactual is adequate ground for the assertion that the spheres are distinct, then (the Leibnizian would surely say) it describes a difference between the two spheres that makes them discernible. If the latter is denied, on the other hand, then how can the counterfactual support the conclusion that the spheres are distinct?

We may give the argument another form to show that nothing hinges on the trustworthiness of our imagination. The Leibnizian's opponent may say: I have described a world, and the description is logically self-consistent; therefore, it is a possible world. The Leibnizian's answer is then: That description is self-consistent only as long as you deny the principle of the identity of indiscernibles. The opponent can then rephrase his appeal to a counterfactual conditional by saying: But the world I described can be embedded in a world that is

possible also according to your principles; since the world I
described is produced merely by omitting something from the
latter, possible world, *it* must also be a possible world. Here
the Leibnizian can answer: You do not take relations seriously
enough; relations to a third thing may be all that distinguishes
the two spheres. Therefore, this simple omission may rad-
ically alter the structure of the possible world. (We might add
that the opponent is perhaps covertly thinking of this omission
as an act in time—that is, that the world originally described
comes to be when this third element is annihilated. But that
would not be a case in point at all, for then the two spheres
would be distinguished through their past history.)

Granting the soundness of Leibniz's reply, we come to the
second question: Suppose, for example, that the accepted cosmological theory implies a perfect determinism, and suppose
we have reason to believe that the world is in a state for which
the theory predicts an eventual return. Does Bois' argument
reveal an absurdity here? Not at all. The Newtonian would
conclude that world history consists of an unending series of
cycles, identical except for their place in time. But if the
theory rules out a beginning, and indeed any asymmetry of
past and future cosmic evolution, the Leibnizian corrects the
Newtonian: Only one such cycle occurs; world history is finite.

We must emphasize, though, that our premises ruled out a
beginning or end. Hence, the conclusion that world history is
finite must be amplified to "finite but unbounded." In other
words, the conclusion is that the order of the states of the universe is that of the points on a circle rather than that of the
points on a line.[6] And this conclusion is reached via the relational theory of time, since the premise of an absolute time
would block the application of the principle of the identity of
indiscernibles. Therefore, the conclusion is, identically, that
the topological structure of time is that of a circle rather than a
line: time is topologically closed.

Neither Nietzsche nor Bois conceived of this possibility.
Charles S. Peirce seems to have been the first to understand
fully the conceivable alternatives for the topological structure
of time.[7]

This is, of course, a radical departure from the traditional
concept of time. And this departure does not hinge on the

acceptance of such speculative, questionable cosmological hypotheses as those we have used to bring it out. Rather the important point is that for the relational theory of time, the possibility of a topologically closed time exists. What has been shown here is that from the original philosophical position that time and world history are not independent, that the structure of time is a function of the structure of the universe and the laws of its development, this possibility follows.

c. Closed Time and Time Order

We recall that the efforts of Leibniz, Kant, and Lechalas to develop a theory of time order did not succeed. It is important to point out that the possibility of a closed time must change the aims of any such theory. For the very relations of *before* and *between* do not make equal sense here. Some of the properties of the relation *before* are:

If A is before B, then B is not before A (*asymmetry*);
If A is before B and B before C, then A is before C (*transitivity*).

Such a relation can exist among the points of a circle, but only provided we restrict its scope. For example, we might add that in Figure 1, A is before B, and B is before C, and A is before C, but no point is before any other point except as we have now indicated. Indeed, we need only exempt one point on the circle from this ordering to remain consistent. For example, let us give a real number as coordinate to every point except D, and say: X is *before* Y if and only if $c(X)$ is less than $c(Y)$. We are still consistent. We can go even further and give D the coordinate $c(D) = 5$. But now the question is: Why is D not before A? The principle seemed to be that X is before Y if you can reach X from Y by going counterclockwise along the circle. But this rule does not hold for D; D is a singularity. Were we to say also that D is before A, we would have a contradiction: A is before C and C is before D, so A is before D. But we said that *before* is asymmetric, and this contradicts the conclusion that D is before A and A before D. Of course, the numbers we used as coordinates are those in the interval $(0,5]$ and these correspond to a line segment bounded on one end, not to a

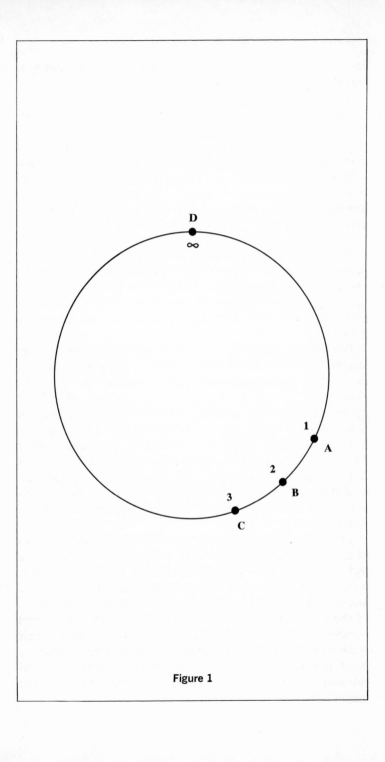

Figure 1

circle. *Before* is a relation suited to an open curve, not to a closed one.

A similar argument can be given for *between*. Intuitively, you might say that *B* is between *A* and *C* because you can go from *A* through *B* to *C* along the circle. But by that criterion, *A* is also between *B* and *C*. Indeed, by that criterion, any point on the circle is between any two other points. And the only way to remedy this is to pick arbitrarily a point, say *D*, to be a singularity in the ordering. To say that *D* is a singularity, however, ipso facto implies that there is a more basic ordering that is inadequately reflected in the *between* (respectively, *before*) ordering.

But what ordering relation is more basic than *before* or *between*? The answer is: the relation of *pair separation*. On the above circle, we can say that the pair of points $(A;C)$ separates the pair $(B;D)$. It is clear intuitively that if you wish to go along the circle from *B* to *D*, you must pass through either *A* or *C*.

The order of points on a line is an order that may be characterized in terms of *between* or *before*. (The difference between these characterizations will be taken up in Section 3.) Equivalently, it can be represented by giving each point a numerical coordinate, in such a way that *numerically less than* corresponds to *before* and *numerically between* corresponds to *between* on the line. This is the technique of *coordinatization:* Each point *P* has a coordinate $c(P)$, and *Q* lies between *P* and *R* if and only if $c(Q)$ is numerically between $c(P)$ and $c(R)$, that is, $c(P) < c(Q) < c(R)$ or $c(R) < c(Q) < c(P)$. The coordinates used here are real numbers, elements of the real-number system.

The order of points on a circle can be characterized in terms of the relation of pair separation. The question is whether the technique of coordinatization is also applicable here. Can pair separation be represented by a mathematical relation? The answer is Yes: we must, then, take as coordinates the elements of the *extended real-number system*. These are just the real numbers, with one special element, designated as ∞. This symbol represents infinity, and the special element is called the point at infinity. This is figurative language however; we recall that topological questions are independent of questions of magnitude.

When we assign coordinates from the extended real-number system, it must be done in such a way that if P and Q separate R and S, then their coordinates numerically separate the co-ordinates of R and S. For example, 3 and 7 numerically separate 5 and 0, and also 5 and ∞. In Section 1d, we shall discuss these matters in more detail.

d. Coordinates for Closed Time

The order of points on a closed line was studied by Giovanni Vailati, who laid down the following axioms for the relation of pair separation (we write "$S(x,y/z,w)$" for "x and y separate z and w"):

(a) $S(x,y/z,w)$ if and only if $S(z,w/x,y)$.
(b) $S(x,y/z,w)$ if and only if $S(x,y/w,z)$.
(c) If $S(x,y/z,w)$, then it is not the case that $S(x,z/y,w)$.
(d) If $S(x,y/z,w)$ and $S(x,z/y,v)$, then $S(x,z/w,v)$.
(e) If x,y,z, and w are distinct points, then x is separated from one of the others by the remaining two.

The last condition rules out that the line has the form of a figure eight. Note that if we use x,y,z, and w to refer to events rather than to points, we should "nonsimultaneous" rather than "distinct" above.

Turning now to the coordinates, in the extended real-number system the numerical functions are extended to the special element ∞ through the equation

$$f(\infty) = \lim_{r \to \infty} f(r)$$

To define numerical pair separation, we need first the notion of the *cross ratio* of four elements a,b,x,y of the extended real-number system:

$$R(a,b/x,y) = \frac{x-a}{b-x} \div \frac{y-a}{b-y}.$$

We then say that the pair $(a;b)$ *numerically separates* the pair $(x;y)$ if and only if $R(a,b/x,y)$ is negative. When the elements of the extended real-number system are used to coordinatize a closed curve, we speak of *nonhomogeneous coordinates*.[8]

Two simple examples may help here: 1 and 2 do not separate 3 and 7 because $R(1,2/3,7) = 5/3$, which is not negative. But 1 and 3 separate 2 and ∞, because $R(1,3/2,\infty) = -1$, which is negative.

Finally, we may note that the points on an open curve can also be ordered by pair separation. But then we can further define *betweenness* in terms of separation. In the case of the real numbers, we say simply that x is between a and b if $R(a,b/x,\infty)$ is negative. (Hence, in our second example, 2 is between 1 and 3 according to our definitions, as it should be.) The easiest way to define betweenness on an open curve ordered by S is to assign its points real numbers as coordinates in such a way that S is reflected in numerical pair separation among these coordinates. Then we can say: Point w is between points y and z exactly if its coordinate is numerically between their coordinates.

2. Clocks and the Metric of Time

a. *The Relational Aspect of Quantity*

The Aristotelian theory of time was a theory of duration; Leibniz's most original contribution to the subject was to attempt a theory of time order. Indeed, whereas Aristotle characterized time as a measure, Leibniz said it was an order, the order of noncontemporaneous events. But just how does a relational theory of time, designed to explicate temporal order, deal with temporal magnitude?

The followers of Newton saw here a major objection to Leibniz's theory. In his Third Reply to Leibniz, Clarke says categorically that "space and time are quantities; which situation and order are not."[9] In his Fourth Reply, he insists that Leibniz answer the objection; so Leibniz does, though rather cryptically:

> I answer, that order also has its quantity; there is in it, that which goes before, and that which follows; there is distance or interval. Relative things have their quantity as well as absolute ones. For

instance, ratios or proportions in mathematics, have their quantity. . . .[10]

The analogy to ratios is not that fortunate, and Clarke's reply shows this rather well (Leibniz died before he could write a sixth letter). But just what did Leibniz mean by "order also has its quantity"?

A partial answer is given in a later paragraph in the same letter:

> The author objects here, that time cannot be an order of successive things, because the quantity of time may become greater or less, and yet the order of successions continue the same. I answer; this is not so. For if the time is greater, there will be more successive and like states interposed; and if it be less so, there will be fewer. . . .[11]

This answer does begin to refute the common opinion, voiced by Clarke, that "the distance, interval, or quantity of time or space, wherein one thing follows another, is entirely a distinct thing from situation or order."[12] For if we have a number of things arranged in a row, $A_1 A_2 \ldots A_k$, we do get a notion of the magnitude by simply counting—the magnitude of the interval between A_i and A_j being defined here as the number of elements between A_i and A_j. But this is certainly not a sufficient answer. For there is first the possibility that each element has an intrinsic magnitude (say, to the effect that A_2 is twice as big as A_4). And second, there is the possibility that the elements in question do not form a discrete order but a continuum. This is particularly relevant to the passage cited above: Leibniz held that change is continuous, so that there really can be no question of counting the "states interposed."

We find Leibniz's final answer to this problem in the essay "The Metaphysical Foundations of Mathematics," written during approximately the same period as the correspondence with Clarke but not published until almost 200 years later. There Leibniz attempts to reconstruct the foundations of geometry as a theory of relations and order, and he clearly sees the problem of a transition to a theory of continuous magnitude. First, he attempts to characterize the difference between quantity and quality:

> *Quantity* or magnitude is that determination of things which *can be known in things only through their immediate contemporaneous togetherness* (*or through their simultaneous observation*). For example, it is impossible to know what the foot and yard are if there is not available an actually given object applied as a standard to compare different objects. What "a foot" is can, therefore, not be explained completely by definition, i.e., by one which does not contain a determination of the same sort. For we may always say that a foot consists of 12 inches, but the same question arises again concerning the inch, and we have made no progress.[13]

Very important here is the insistence that a determination of quantity presupposes an "immediate contemporaneous togetherness." This makes quantity a matter of comparison: any judgment to the effect "X is this big" must be equivalent to some comparative judgment "X is this much bigger than (as big as) a certain (standard) Y." Second, Leibniz insists that this comparison must be one made in coincidence, in temporal and spatial togetherness. (Note that coincidence is a notion of order.)

There are cases in which this presupposition of "immediate contemporaneous togetherness" is automatically satisfied, namely, when one of the two things compared is a part of the other:

> If a part of a quantity is equal to the whole of another quantity, then the first is called the *greater,* the second the *smaller.* Whence *the whole is greater than the part.*[14]

In this passage, the conclusion that the whole is greater than any of its parts is deduced from the explicit principle "If a part of X is equal to Y, then X is greater than Y" and the tacit principle "Everything is equal to itself." But suppose Y is not part of X. How can we arrive at the premise that Y is equal to part of X?

Leibniz's answer is that if Y is in coincidence with part of X, this premise holds; but if this condition of coincidence is not satisfied we must either bring X and Y into coincidence or use some external standard and bring it into coincidence with each. It is important to appreciate how this is an answer to the question What role can the notion of quantity have in a theory that begins with relations and order? For Leibniz is saying, in effect, that the study of quantity must also be a study of relation—of the relation of equality of magnitude (congruence). This relation of congruence, plus the nonmetric part-whole relation, will suffice to define *greater than* and also *N times greater than*. To get from this point to such quantitative judgments as "The field is two acres large" or "The process lasted two hours" one must choose a standard, a unit measure; and this choice cannot be embodied in a nominal definition, but must involve the exhibition or designation of some empirical entity.

This reduces all questions about metric to questions about the congruence relation. Here Leibniz insists that the determination of congruence presupposes a coincidence ("immediate contemporaneous togetherness"). It appears that Roger Boscovitch was the first to raise questions about the fulfillment of this presupposition, in the form of the question Are we justified in assuming that a wooden or iron 10-foot rod is the same length after it has been moved?[15]

Consider in particular two successive periods of the same pendulum. These, *ex hypothesi,* cannot enjoy such coincidences. Hence, we must use some external standard, say, a clock—that is, we must choose some periodic process to serve as standard, and define its period to be of unit length. But which periodic process should we choose for this? Is there a right choice or a wrong choice? Surely the question of congruence will arise again for the successive periods of whatever process we choose as standard—if the question of a right choice makes sense here.

Leonhard Euler discussed this question in *Réflections sur l'espace et le temps.*[16] He proposed the following criterion: A process is truly periodic if when we take it as marking the unit of time, then Newton's first law of motion is satisfied. (This is the law of inertia, whch states that a moving body that is not affected by [unbalanced] external forces travels equal distances in equal amounts of time.)

Newton's mechanics constituted by this time (the middle of the eighteenth century) a well-confirmed and highly respected scientific theory. Hence, Euler seems to be proposing an objective, empirical criterion, supported by exactly the evidence that leads us to accept the Newtonian laws of motion. But if we accept Euler's criterion for the suitability of a chosen clock, what happens to the law of inertia? We have then agreed to choose our clocks in such a way that their findings necessarily confirm this law; any putative counterexample to the law will be viewed as proving that we used the wrong kind of clock. But then this law is no longer a factual, empirical assertion: not the way the world is but what we have decided to mean by "The clock runs evenly" guarantees its truth.

Suppose we were to use a nonstandard clock that gives the reading $f(t) = u$ when our usual clock reads t. If the function f is not too complicated, we can easily rewrite the laws of motion in terms of u rather than t. The old laws would be correct by the old clocks, and the new laws by the new clocks. But, of course, the two sets of laws would say objectively the same; only the language would be different. Then why choose the former?

The first answer is the historical one that we have always regarded certain processes as periodic and that these agree with each other and hence provide a set of readily available clocks. That this does not provide a sufficient explanation was emphasized by Poincaré.[17] After all, even if we do not have a clock that runs at the rate $f(t)$, we certainly could decide to use the variable $u = f(t)$, rather than t, in theoretical physics. Indeed, we might have good theoretical reasons for this: reasons of simplicity and mathematical convenience. In a certain sense, we actually do this, Poincaré pointed out: since Newton, we do not consider the natural clocks (unquestioningly accepted before Newton) as running exactly evenly. We correct them to offset the perturbations due to external forces, to which science declares them to be subject.

Thus, astronomers correct their chronometers for temperature, air resistance, and such, and accept the sidereal day (duration of the rotation of the earth as measured by the apparent movement of the stars) as standard. But this, too, they regard as not perfectly accurate, because of the influence of the tides; Newtonian science declares that the tides affect the constancy of the rotation of the earth. Why not retain the old clocks (accept the sidereal day as the real standard) and correct the laws of dynamics? Because then our science would become complicated beyond belief:

The definition implicitly adopted by the astronomers may be summed up thus: Time should be so defined that the equations of mechanics may be as simple as possible. In other words, there is not one way of measuring time more true than another; that which is generally adopted is only more convenient.[18]

The conclusion is therefore, that quantity consists in certain relations, especially congruence, and in particular congruence with a standard; the choice of this standard is essentially conventional in the case of time.

b. Conventional and Objective Elements in Definition

The words in which Poincaré summarized his conclusion, "Time should be so defined that the equations of mechanics may be as simple as possible," are perhaps somewhat misleading. The historical process is rather that data are gathered from measurement by traditional clocks; hypotheses are proposed to give a systematic account of these data; the clocks are then corrected in accordance with these hypotheses, and the data reinterpreted accordingly. (This aspect of scientific investigation is sometimes called a hermeneutic circle or spiral. The interaction of measurement and hypothesis in such investigation is especially apparent in the procedure discussed by Adolf Grünbaum.[19]) To place the condition on scientific hypotheses that they must not require a reinterpretation of the data of measurement would indeed overcomplicate the business of science. On the other hand, there is also a law of diminishing returns for theoretical simplification.

But the important conclusion is that the assertion that two time intervals are equal in magnitude makes sense only with reference to a standard of temporal congruence, which must be independently specified. In that sense, this magnitude is not intrinsic in the way that the number of marbles in a certain collection is an intrinsic feature of that collection. The specification of a standard or temporal congruence—a clock— is not itself a factual assertion. It does not mean that the chosen clock is truly periodic—but only that it will be used, by stipulation, as the standard for what will be called periodic.

Here, however, we must note a very important point about stipulations or definitions. Even a purely stipulative definition may have a factual presupposition. For example, a definition of the form

(1) By definition, $X = Y$ if and only if Y has the property F

presupposes that there is at most one thing that has the property F. A specific example of (1) is the following definition of a number n:

(2) By definition, $X = n$ if and only if $x^2 = x^3$

This has a false presupposition. For $0^2 = 0^3 \, (= 0)$, and also $1^2 = 1^3 \, (= 1)$. Therefore, this definition would lead us to the proof:

(3) $0 = n$
        $1 = n$
hence, $0 = 1$

If we find that a definition has a presupposition, we may precede the definition by a postulate or proof that the presupposition is true or rephrase the definition to eliminate the presupposition. (This is a subject in logic, and we need not go into it here.)

As Poincaré pointed out, the definition of temporal congruence may also have such a factual presupposition.[20] Suppose the following definition is proposed for the unit of duration:

(4) One unit of time is, by definition, the magnitude of the time interval that elapses between the emission and return of a light signal that travels through a vacuum and is reflected by a mirror exactly 1 meter from its source.

Such a light clock is easy to construct. But suppose we allow the clock to turn on its axis, so that the light does not always travel in the same direction. Better yet, let us have two such light clocks side by side, one turned at an angle to the other.

Will they agree? The above definition presupposes that they will. This is an empirical assertion; in fact, it contradicts the nineteenth-century theory of the existence of ether. An experiment was devised by Albert A. Michelson and Edward W. Morley to test this assertion; to everyone's surprise the experiment confirmed it (we shall discuss this experiment in Chapter V).

Let us give an exact statement of what is presupposed here: When a certain kind of process is accepted as a standard of temporal congruence, it is presupposed that if two members of this kind are brought into coincidence they agree ("equivalence" in the sense of Poincaré). This comparison of duration between coincident processes is not conventional, as Leibniz already saw. In fact, it belongs entirely to the subject of temporal order, for the assertion

(5) Process A and process B have the same duration.

is in this case equivalent to

(6) Process A and process B occupy the same time interval.

—that is,

(7) The beginnings of A and B are simultaneous, and the ends of A and B are simultaneous.

or, eliminating reliance on the before-after distinction,

(8) The extrema of A and B are pairwise simultaneous.

The conventional element that we emphasized above enters only when the two processes are not coincident.

The conclusion is, then, that the time metric is conventional in that we choose the standard of congruence (which may be an actual process or kind of process, or else calculable in terms of an actual process and a certain theory). But there is also an objective element; the choice of a kind of clock may have certain factual presuppositions, which must be true.

c. The Poincaré-Russell Debate

In 1897 Russell published his *Essay on the Foundations of Geometry*, which was the subject of a critical review by Poincaré. Russell wrote a reply, and Poincaré a rejoinder.[21] It must be noted that Russell was an idealist when he wrote the essay, but he was in complete rebellion against idealism during this debate with Poincaré. Also, the debate centered largely on space and geometry, but we shall attempt to ferret out what pertains to time.

Russell states his views on time in Section 151 of the essay. This section is largely a restatement of the views of Bernard Bosanquet. We shall first summarize Bosanquet's statement on the subject, to bring out a first point of disagreement between Poincaré on one hand and Bosanquet and Russell on the other. Then we shall quote from the essay to bring out a second point of disagreement.

Briefly, Bosanquet argues as follows: Measurement of duration can only take the form of comparison with a clock—a process *chosen* as marking equal intervals. If we have several candidates for such a standard, the question that is the correct one is "unmeaning." So far there is no disagreement with Poincaré. But then Bosanquet considers the assertion

> (9) There is no periodic process all of whose periods have equal duration (after correction for external influences).

It follows from the above, he says, that this assertion is absurd. For if time measurement can consist only in comparison with a standard, then this assertion amounts to the proposition that no process is truly periodic when compared with a further standard that *ex hypothesi* does not exist.[22]

Bosanquet was arguing against the view that temporal magnitude is something intrinsic and does not merely consist in the relation to a stipulated standard of congruence. But the above argument goes too far, from Poincaré's point of view. According to Poincaré, we may choose any metric at all for time, for the sake of theoretical simplicity. Here Bosanquet appears to ignore the possibility that a measurement may involve not only comparison but also calculation. When this fact is noted, one can easily conceive a metric by which (9) is true.

For example, suppose that we have heretofore used a clock C, by which each event X has a date (time coordinate) $t(X)$. Now we adopt a new form of time reckoning by which we give each event X a coordinate $t'(X)$ such that

$$t'(X) = \log t(X)$$

and such that the magnitude of the time interval between X and Y is

$$|\, t'(X) - t'(Y)\, |$$

There may well be *no* process whose periods are equal by this definition. Yet the proposal is not at all absurd, since we have a straightforward way of determining temporal magnitudes: first, we use the clock C, and then we calculate by the formula $t' = \log t$.

But if Bosanquet and Russell were to agree that t' provides an acceptable metric, they would still not have committed themselves to the point of view that *any* metric is in principle acceptable. Specifically, they would not accept a metric that is explicitly dependent on temporal position. Here we may quote Russell:

> No day can be brought into temporal coincidence with any other day, to show that the two exactly cover each other; we are therefore reduced to the arbitrary assumption that some motion or set of motions, given us in experience, is uniform. . . .
>
> But here . . . another possibility is mathematically open to us, and can only be excluded by its philosophic absurdity; we might have assumed that the above set of approximately agreeing motions all had velocities which varied approximately as some arbitrarily assumed function of the time, $f(t)$ say, measured from some arbitrary origin. . . . Such a hypothesis *is* mathematically possible, but it is excluded logically by the comparative nature of the judgement of quantity, and philosophically by the fact that it involves absolute time, as a determining agent in change. . . .[23]

Russell's logical argument from "the comparative nature of

the judgement of quantity" is essentially that of Bosanquet, which we have just discussed.

Russell's philosophical argument raises a different point: if by our new time reckoning all processes speed up with time (for example), then this acceleration must have a cause. Since the only correlated variation is in temporal position, this cause must be time itself. But the idea of a causally efficacious absolute time is absurd, according to Russell. (At the very least, it would be an unwarranted assumption, leading to all sorts of theoretical difficulties.)

The argument is predicated on the assumption that any acceleration must have a cause. Well, did not Newton in his highly successful science of dynamics postulate exactly that? This must have been the reason in Russell's mind. But Newton only postulated that any accelerations *as measured by the clocks that he accepted* are proportional to unbalanced forces. If we switch to a new time metric, say $t' = f(t)$, then we have, in effect, switched to a different language to report the same empirical facts. Newton's second law of motion states that acceleration measured by $t = f^{-1}(t')$ is proportional to an unbalanced force. It does not say this for acceleration as measured by $t' = f(t)$.

For example, the usual definition for the metric of time will say:

> For events X and Y such that $t(X) \leq t(Y)$, the magnitude of the interval $(t(X), t(Y))$ is
>
> $$d(X,Y) = |\, t(Y) - t(X)\,| \,.$$

Suppose we decide to use the alternative metric given by

> For events X, Y such that $t(X) \leq t(Y)$, the magnitude of the interval $(t(X), t(Y))$ is
>
> $$d'(X,Y) = |\, t(X) + 1/2(t(Y) - t(X))\,| \,.$$

By this new metric, all processes that are periodic by the old metric slow down with time, up to a certain instant; after that they speed up with time. It is certainly not part of Newton's dynamics that *this* acceleration varies directly with a certain (unknown) force. If anyone adopts this new metric, then he cannot find the correct consequences of Newton's laws until he has translated those laws into his new language (in which "temporal congruence" has a new meaning).

This means also, of course, that the adoption of a new metric must be accompanied by a specification of how to measure durations as specified by it, and hence a translation into the old metric. Had Poincaré emphasized this point more, Alfred North Whitehead, a later English critic, might not have thought that the following contradicts his point of view:

> . . . we have, in fact, presented to our senses a definite set of transformations forming a congruence group, resulting in a set of measure relations which are in no respect arbitrary. Accordingly our scientific laws are to be stated relevantly to that particular congruence group.[24]

As we mentioned above, Russell debated these questions with Poincaré at a time when he had definitely turned from idealism to realism. His revolt against those whom he had followed before 1898 was so enthusiastic that he "began to believe everything the Hegelians disbelieved."[25] Accordingly, his arguments there are not those which his essay would lead us to expect. They are rather to the effect that duration must be an intrinsic feature of a process and has nothing to do with comparison. Since the Hegelians did not accept the reality of Newton's absolute time, Russell did; but after that "first fine careless rapture" he gradually came to a more balanced view.[26]

3. The Anisotropy of Time

a. The Temporal Perspective of Past and Future

We are now going to discuss the very important, but elusive concept of *direction*. If asked "In what direction is Boston?" I would answer "North." This would be a correct answer, because it is made in New Haven. But if I were asked the question while in Halifax, I would answer "South." So the notion of the direction of Boston is incomplete; for example, it is elliptic for the direction of Boston from New Haven. Furthermore, the directions north and south do not represent relations between any two places, but only between places on the earth. For example, the question whether the sun is or is not north of the star Sirius makes no sense. On the other hand, we could invent a system of cosmic directions; it would require only that we choose some bodies as points of reference, just as we choose the North Star as point of reference for the earth. In fact when the earth was believed to be the center of the universe, the geographic directions were extended to the whole universe. There are vestiges of this in ordinary discourse ("The sun rises in the east.") and in astrology ("At the beginning of April, the sun is in Aries").

In time there are also directions: past and future. If asked "In what temporal direction lies the World War II?" I can appropriately answer "In the past." The answer is correct in part because it is made in 1969, but it would not have been correct in 1934. Therefore, the notion of the temporal direction of X is incomplete; it is elliptic for the temporal direction of *X* from *Y*.

We may note a lack of parallelism here in the English language: for the case of time, we have a special locution when the direction is relative to the utterance of the answer:

(1a) Boston is north of here.
       (Boston is north of the place of this utterance.)
(1b) World War II is in the past.
       (World War II is before the time of this utterance.)
(2a) Boston is north of New Haven.
(2b) World War II is before the Korean War.

Note that in both (1a), subjective case for space, and (2a), objective case for space, we use "north of." But in (1b) we use "past" and in (2b) we use "before;" we do not say "*X* is to the past of *Y*."

This grammatical difference has often been thought to reflect a difference in fact. Bergson accused earlier philosophers of having spatialized time in thinking that time is somehow the *dual* of space. The example above shows that temporal discourse is not merely dual to spatial discourse in English— but might this be a historical accident in the development of the English language? (We could use "to the past of" for "before," after all.)

But consider the following:

(3a) When persons P_1 and P_2 say "here" at one and the same time, they do not in general refer to the same place.

(3b) When persons P_1 and P_2 say "now" at one and the same time, they do refer to the same time.

Does this not show a disanalogy? Does it not show that "now" is somehow the same for everyone, in a sense in which "here" is not? But (3b) does not deny the dual of (3a). The dual of (3a) is

(3c) When persons P_1 and P_2 say "now" in one and the same place, they do not in general refer to the same time.

And that is perfectly true. Consider a polite conversation (in one place) in which no two people speak at the same time.

Another idea for a factual disanalogy between time and space is that we can move in space: we can be south of Boston and, through some exertion, come to be north of Boston. But we cannot be after World War II and come to be before World War II: time travel is not possible.

This idea needs to be disentangled; especially since, as any reader of science fiction knows, time travel certainly appears to be conceivable (although the notion has also generated some paradoxes). The above argument seems to involve another failure to dualize correctly. Let us begin with

(4a) At t_1, P_1 was north of Boston, and at a later time t_2, P_1 was south of Boston.

This assertion expresses the fact that P_1 moved from one place to another. Now the dual of this is not the absurd

(4b) At t_1, World War II was in the past for P_1, and at a later time t_2, World War II was in the future for P_1.

Rather, the dual of (4a) is

(4c) In place q_1, World War II was in the past for P_1, and

at another place q_2 to the north of q_1, World War II
was in the future for P_1.

And sentence (4c) would be true, for example, if P_1 lived in
Boston until 1939 and lived in New Haven from 1946 on.
What is confusing is only that motion, which is change of place
with time, does have an important place in our ordinary conceptual scheme, but the dual notion of change of time with
place is very contrived and has no place in our ordinary conceptual scheme.[27]   Of course, there must be a reason for that;
perhaps the reason is that we are not actually able to engage
in time travel of the (nontrivial) sort described in science-
fiction stories.

Be that as it may, the objective before-after direction appears much more important to us than any direction in space.
And so the question very naturally arose: Is there not a physical basis for this direction?

We have seen that Leibniz thought of *before* as a basic
temporal relation, to be explicated on the basis of the cause-
effect relation.   Were such an attempt successful, no separate
physical basis need be found for *temporally between* or *simultaneous* for these can be defined in terms of *before*.   In this century, Reichenbach made the same attempt.   He agreed that
we cannot be as uncritical about the notion of cause as Leibniz
had been; after all, we must face Hume's criticisms of this notion.   Accordingly, Reichenbach attempted to explicate the
notion X is the cause of Y; he used for this a method he called
the *mark method*.   Since the method was entirely unsuccessful,
we shall not stop to consider it here (although we shall return
to it briefly in Chapter VI).

If it is not possible to find a physical counterpart to the
before-after relation, we can still proceed as with space—that
is, we can take for granted the relation of between (or of pair
separation), hope to find a physical counterpart for it, and then
introduce temporal direction in the way in which the geograph-
ical directions are introduced for things on the surface of the
earth.   This would mean that we would use points of reference
in time, just as we use the North Star; for example, we could
stipulate that the birth of Christ is *before* the death of Christ.
(This would accord with common usage, as the reader may
check for himself.)

But here an interesting question was raised by philosophers of science. In physics, the directions north and south do not appear, because no specific body or place on earth plays a role in physics. Similarly, neither the birth and death of Christ, nor any other events, play a role in physics; hence, the conventional definitions of *before* would not be possible there. But the before-after relation does appear in physics. Does that not show that temporal directions are not analogous to direction in space?

What it suggests is that a definition of temporal direction is possible, which makes no essential reference to a conventionally chosen point of reference. How would such a definition proceed? It would have to point to some asymmetry in natural processes, in the historical development of the world. For example, suppose there is some natural process X whose instances X_i always have the form

$$X_i = (A_i B_i C_i D_i)$$

and never occur in the reverse $(D_i C_i B_i A_i)$. Then, supposing that temporal betweenness is given, we might define:

> E is before F if and only if there is an instance $X_i = (A_i B_i C_i D_i)$ of X such that F is between E and A_i, and A_i is between F and D_i.

(This definition has a factual presupposition; the reader should try to ferret this out.) A process such as X is called *irreversible*. Are there irreversible processes? Of course: sickness, old age, death, combustion, digestion—there are many examples of common processes that we cannot reverse.

But returning to physics, the question is whether these processes simply do not occur in the reverse or whether they cannot, as a matter of physical impossibility. Presumably, if the laws of physics do not rule out the reversibility of such processes, then for all we know their reverse might eventually occur.*

Here it is found that the laws of mechanics do not entail the

---

* This argument is not quite correct. Cosmology might lead to the conclusion that even if all natural processes are reversible as far as physical laws are concerned, the boundary conditions are nevertheless such that world history has a certain asymmetry. But cosmology is still a speculative subject.

irreversibility of any process. (This is true not only for classical but also for quantum mechanics and relativistic mechanics.) But in another branch of physics, thermodynamics, which studies such prima facie irreversible processes as combustion, mixing, and chemical reactions, we might expect to find such asymmetry implied.

The problem whether such asymmetries exist is known as the problem of *the anisotropy of time* (sometimes "direction of time" or "arrow of time" or even "flow of time"; these terms are rather misleading). Space is considered to be *isotropic* because we do not believe there is any pervasive or systematic asymmetry in the spatial structure of the universe. If, similarly, our physics does not imply any pervasive or systematic asymmetry in the temporal evolution of the universe, we shall hold time to be isotropic also. In that case, the relations of before and after, the temporal directions of past and future, will have essentially no more importance than the relations defined by the compass. They will then be definable only through points of reference conventionally chosen, and important only in view of the local conditions of our epoch. And they will appear in physics only because of the convenience of relating the time variable to clocks in common use. On the other hand, if our physics does entail such a pervasive asymmetry, then we shall hold time to be anisotropic.

A final word before we turn to thermodynamics: with this discussion we shall enter the twentieth century. But most of the discussion (and all of that part with which we are concerned) is independent of the peculiarly twentieth-century developments in physics (relativity and quantum theory).

b. Thermodynamics and Physical Irreversibility

(i) Phenomenological Thermodynamics   Thermodynamics was developed in the beginning of the nineteenth century, especially through the work of Nicholas Leonard Sadi Carnot. Any physical theory deals with physical systems, and we speak of a *mechanical system* when the theory is mechanics, a *thermodynamic system* when the theory is thermodynamics, a *biological system* when the theory is biology, and so on. A thermodynamic system is just a system regarded from the point of view of thermodynamics. And that means: character-ized in terms of the properties that are studied in thermo-dynamics. The same holds for the notion of *thermodynamic state:* the thermodynamic state of a gas at a time t is given by specifying the pressure P, its volume V, and its temperature T at time t—because those are the physical magnitudes dealt with in thermodynamics.

Thermodynamics took over some concepts from mechanics, particularly, the concept of *work*. Work is defined precisely in mechanics as the product of force and distance. For example, suppose I push an object for a distance of 1 yard. Depending on the weight of the object, I have to exert more or less force. The more force I exert, the more work I do. If I now push another object with the same force, but through a distance of 2 yards, again I do more work. The amount of work done equals the force exerted multiplied by the distance through which the object is moved.

Work is one way in which the state of a system may be changed. Suppose I have a gas in a container with a piston, and I push the piston with a certain force through a certain distance. Then, I have performed a certain amount of work on the gas (the system) and thereby changed its state (its vol-ume is decreased and its pressure increased). Another way to change the state of a system is by applying heat to it. If I put the container of gas above a flame, then a certain amount of heat is applied to it, and its state is changed (its temperature and its pressure both increase). The third important concept of thermodynamics is *energy*. Energy is, essentially, the ability to do work. Suppose I heat the gas in the container with the piston and then let go of the piston. The gas then pushes the piston up. The reason is that heating the gas gave it more en-ergy, and it was then able to do work (to move the piston through a certain distance).

The energy that a system has is a function of its state. And here we may state the first law of thermodynamics, which has two parts:

(1a) In an isolated system, the sum of all forms of energy remains constant.

(1b) In a closed system, the increase in energy (through a

change of state) is equal to the work done on the system plus the heat absorbed by it:

$$\Delta U = \Delta Q + \Delta W$$

Here *closed* means that no matter can enter or leave the system; *isolated* means that neither matter nor energy can enter or leave the system; and ΔU, ΔQ, and ΔW stand for the increments in energy, heat, and work, respectively. (The reader may note that [1a] is a corollary of [1b].)

It is important to note that in (1a) we said "all forms of energy." There is mechanical energy (that of a coiled spring or a moving flywheel), thermal energy (that of a hot radiator), chemical energy, and so on. Consider the following examples: (*i*) Two metal bars at different temperatures are brought together and then isolated from their surroundings; their temperatures become the same (somewhere between their original temperatures). (*ii*) A rotating flywheel comes to rest due to the friction in its bearings; the temperature of the bearings and wheel rises (the mechanical energy of the wheel is converted into thermal energy by the friction).

These are examples of transitions inside isolated systems. It is noteworthy that the reverses of these processes do not occur. (Of course, we could draw off the heat from the flywheel and its bearings, and set it in motion again. But this can be done only by breaking the isolation and allowing the system to interact with other systems.) But why do these reversed processes not occur? The total energy of the isolated system remains the same; therefore, the reverse process would not violate the first law. There must be some further principle that determines the *direction* in which a process can take place. Although our two examples are quite dissimilar, is there some feature that they have in common?

To put the question very precisely, Given two states of an isolated system, is there a criterion for determining whether some possible process leads from one to the other? This question could be answered if there were some property of the state that is different at the beginning and end of a *possible* process. This property cannot be the energy, since that remains the same in an isolated system. But such a property was found: it is called the *entropy*.

If a system receives a quantity of heat ΔQ while it is at a temperature T (on the absolute scale), its entropy is increased by

$$\Delta S = \frac{\Delta Q}{T}$$

Now the *second law of thermodynamics* says that

(2) No change occurring in an isolated system can result in a decrease in the entropy of the system.

Thus, some processes in an isolated system will lead to states of the same entropy, and others will lead to states of higher entropy. In the latter case, the reverse is not a possible process.

Thus, in example (*i*), let the bars be B_1 and B_2 at temperatures $T_1 > T_2$. Then B_1 gives up a certain amount of heat ΔQ, and B_2 has an increment of ΔQ, and B_1 an increment of $-\Delta Q$. Let S_1 be the entropy for B_1 and S_2 the entropy for B_2. Then, by the definition of the increment of entropy we have:

$$\Delta S_1 = \frac{-\Delta Q}{T_1} \text{ and } \Delta S_2 = \frac{\Delta Q}{T_2}$$

The total change in the entropy of the complex isolated system comprising B_1 and B_2 is then

$$\Delta S_1 + \Delta S_2 = \frac{-\Delta Q}{T_1} + \frac{\Delta Q}{T_2}$$

$$= \Delta Q \left(\frac{1}{T_2} - \frac{1}{T_1} \right) < 0$$

Hence, in this change the entropy increased, and the second law predicts, apparently quite correctly, that the reverse process cannot occur.

The entropy of a system is to some extent reflected in the form of the energy that it has. When mechanical energy is transformed into heat, as in example (*ii*), the entropy always increases. Hence, heat is called *low grade* energy; mechanical energy is *high grade* (electrical energy is also high grade and chemical energy medium grade). We make this more intuitive as follows: If the heat generated by the friction in example (*ii*) were used to drive the flywheel (via a steam engine), it *could not* make the flywheel go as fast as it orginally did (no matter how efficient the steam engine). For this reason, Kelvin called the second law the principle of the *degradation of energy*. If this law is entirely correct, the universe must be slowly dying a heat death: all forms of energy will finally be converted into heat, and the world will reach thermal equilibrium, from which it can never emerge. That would certainly make time anisotropic.

(ii) Thermodynamics and Statistical Mechanics The hypothesis was offered as early as the seventeenth century that the peculiarly thermodynamic properties of heat and temperature were somehow related to molecular motion. There were, however, a number of factors that made scientists in the nineteenth century regard the hypothesis as unfruitful: first, the success of the "phenomenological" methods; second, the undesirability of postulating hypothetical entities such as molecules; and third, that similar mechanistic hypotheses concerning electrical, magnetic, and chemical phenomena were quite unsuccessful. But this hypothesis continued to be explored and turned out to be particularly fruitful in gas theory; by the end of the nineteenth century, thermodynamics could be said to have been reduced to statistical mechanics.

In this connection, consider the perfect gas law:

$$PV = RT$$

(here R is a constant [the gas constant]). The quantities of pressure, P, and volume, V, are also encountered in mechanics. In mechanics we can deduce a relation between the pressure and volume of the gas, and the mean kinetic energy E of the molecules of the gas:

$$PV = \frac{2NE}{3}$$

(here N is the number of molecules in one gram molecule of the gas [Avogadro's number]). From these two equations we can immediately deduce

$$RT = \frac{2NE}{3}$$

that is,

$$T = \frac{2NE}{3R}$$

which expresses the temperature of the gas in terms of the kinetic energy of the molecules. In other words, a non-mechanical property of the gas as a whole has been expressed as a function of a purely mechanical property of its constituent molecules.

Of course, a volume of gas has a lot of molecules, all rushing here and there in a most disorganized way. It is not feasible, therefore, to apply the laws of motion directly to this very complex system, which is why statistical methods were developed at this point. The fulcrum for the application of this method is provided by the *quasi-ergodic hypothesis*. This was merely a plausible hypothesis in the nineteenth century; it was proved to follow from the principles of classical mechanics in the twentieth century.

To explain the quasi-ergodic hypothesis we must explain the notions of *microstate* and *macrostate*. A single molecule has a position q and momentum p; together, these qualities specify its states. We are given the microstate of the gas (at a time t) if we are given the state of each of its constituent molecules, to within a certain small range. Its macrostates are simply what we called its thermodynamic states before. We can determine a macrostate by means of our measuring instruments: we can measure the pressure and volume of a gas, and also its temperature (or, if you wish, the mean kinetic energy of its molecules). We cannot measure the position or kinetic energy of the individual molecules.

The quasi-ergodic hypothesis is a postulate guaranteeing that each of the microstates is equally probable—that is, if the system is isolated and left alone, then it will in the long run spend equal time in each of its possible microstates. (And which microstates are possible is determined only by the requirements, that the gas remain in the container and its total energy remain constant.) This result is independent of its initial state, and nothing is said here about entropy. How can this be in accord with the second law of thermodynamics?

To answer this question we must know what corresponds to entropy in statistical thermodynamics. There are many more microstates than macrostates, in the sense that our crude instruments can (in principle) distinguish between any two macrostates but not between any two microstates. So if we know that the gas is in macrostate M, we do not yet know which microstate obtains; we know only that it must be one of a class $K(M)$. Now, the magnitude of $K(M)$ varies drastically from macrostate to macrostate, which means that some macrostates are much more probable than others. For example, let there be m microstates. Then, by the quasi-ergodic hypothesis, each microstate has a probability of $1/m$. If $K(M)$ has i members, then the probability of M is i/m.

In other words, the probability of M varies directly with the number of microstates that belong to $K(M)$. Now, the statistical concept of entropy is such that the entropy of a state corresponds to its probability. Thus, the more probable a state, the higher its entropy, and vice versa. This turns out to correspond to the earlier, thermodynamic concept of entropy in all relevant respects.

The most probable states are the equilibrium states. If a system is in equilibrium, and you check it at some time later, the likelihood is that it is still in equilibrium (since no other state is more probable). If the system is not in equilibrium to begin, other states are more probable, and the likelihood is that later it is found in a more probable state—that is, in a state of higher entropy. This is the statistical version of the second law of thermodynamics.

Thus, the reduction of thermodynamics to statistical dynamics leads to a revision of the second law:

(3) A change occurring in an isolated system will most probably lead to a state of greater or equal entropy.

But "most probably" is not "certainly"; and the following also holds:

(4) In the long run, decreases in entropy are as frequent as increases in entropy.

The apparent conflict between (3) and (4) seems to create a paradox. Indeed, this is often referred to as *Loschmidt's paradox,* after the scientist who pointed this out. But there is no real contradiction here.[28]

(iii) Entropy and Temporal Anisotropy The second law of thermodynamics, as originally formulated, would have been eminently suited to a definition of temporal direction. Suppose that the order relations *between* and *simultaneous* have been explicated or are taken for granted. Then we may define a *state* of a system X to be an exhaustive class of simultaneous events involving X. And we may define *later than* as follows: if S_1 and S_2 are states of X and the state S_2 is of higher entropy than S_1, then S_2 is later than S_1—and furthermore, if S_3 is between S_1 and S_2, then either S_1 or S_2 is later than S_3.

But the statistical reformulation of this second law is not suited to this task. Indeed, it entails that low-entropy states devolve *most probably* into higher-entropy states. But this fact is deduced purely on the basis of the absolute probabilities of the macrostates. Hence, we can also deduce that a low-entropy state is most probably also preceded by a high-entropy state. Therefore, we cannot simply define *later than* as the direction of change to higher entropy in most cases.

But how is this to be reconciled with the fact that we witness only changes to higher entropy in natural processes? Ludwig Boltzmann, who developed the statistical concept of entropy in the late nineteenth century, said that the original acceptance of the phenomenological second law reflected only *local* conditions. And he immediately drew the conclusion that there is no physical counterpart to the before-after relation for the universe as a whole. Thermal equilibrium is the most probable state; hence, the universe as a whole is in thermal equilibrium. What we witness here is only a local disturbance:

> Then in the universe, which is in thermal equilibrium throughout and therefore dead, there will occur here and there relatively small

regions of the same size as our galaxy (we call them single worlds) which, during the relatively short time of eons, fluctuate noticeably from thermal equilibrium. . . . For the universe, the two directions of time are indistinguishable, just as in space there is no up and down. However, just as at a particular place on the earth's surface we call "down" the direction toward the center of the earth, so will a living being in a particular time interval of such a single world distinguish the direction of time toward the less probable state from the opposite direction (the former toward the past, the latter toward the future).[29]

This was, of course, speculative cosmology; moreover, the reference to living beings and their sense of before and after is given in the manner of a fable or myth, a heuristic device.

Twentieth-century writers have, on the whole, agreed to the soundness of Boltzmann's reasoning. The asymmetry in natural processes with respect to past and future, so evident in our experience, is not entailed by the laws of physics alone, but is in part due to the boundary conditions in our galactic era. This admission does not mean that there might not be a pervasive asymmetry in the history of the universe as a whole, but it certainly prevents us from considering such an extrapolation necessary.

A major contribution to the discussion of temporal anisotropy is the notion of *branch system,* introduced by Reichenbach and developed by Grünbaum.[30] We say that a system "branches off" when it has been in interaction with its environment and then becomes isolated. Normally, this isolation is not perfect; and normally, the branch system leaves even this relative isolation again in a fairly short time. An example is a rock on the earth heated by the sun during the day, but isolated from this solar radiation during the night. Even the statistical version of the second law entails that

(a) If the branch system is in equilibrium initially, it is most often still in equilibrium when its isolation ceases.

(b) If the branch system is not in equilibrium initially, its entropy increases most often during its isolation.

Here, we cannot add to (b) that its initial state is also preceded by a higher-entropy state, because the branch system simply did not exist as an isolated system before that initial state. So here we have a definite statistical asymmetry. That such branch systems are constantly being formed all around us is, of course, a boundary condition and not the consequence of a law.

Once we settle for this kind of de facto asymmetry due in part to boundary conditions, other examples of physical irreversibility may be found.[31] In addition, we may consider whether these factual asymmetries do not, in fact, extend throughout the history of the universe. This is a question to be settled relative to a cosmological theory—an area of physics in which theories have not as yet enjoyed conclusive success.

On the other hand, there are many ways *for us* to coordinate temporal direction with features of the physical world, as we have seen in Section 3a. Hence, when Boltzmann, on the basis of his reformulation of the second laws of thermodynamics, called the temporal directions of before and after "a mere illusion arising from our specially restricted viewpoint," his position was more audacious than tenable.[32]

4. What Time Is

a. Time and the Mind

The question "What is time?" has a presupposition: that there is such a thing as time. As we argued in Chapter I, we might refuse to accept this presupposition, refuse to give a direct answer of the form "Time is . . ." and instead maintain that time is not a kind of thing at all.

And there is a certain danger in accepting the presupposition. We *might* be led by it into a conceptual muddle such as the following:

> If time is a thing (of any kind), then we can conceive of there being nothing except just that thing. Therefore, the existence of time is independent of the existence of anything else. Hence, Newton's idea of absolute time must be right after all.

We have already encountered a number of fallacies involving the notions of conceivability and possibility, and the argument above will not convince anyone who is on his guard here. In other words, we need not be misled if we accept the question "What is time?" as not being mistaken.

The attempts to give a direct answer to this question may throw some further light on our temporal concepts. We recall that Aristotle defined "time" as "the measure of motion with respect to before and after." This, we decided, is an adequate definition only of duration, since it takes temporal order for granted. But in any case, it is a direct answer to the question "What is time?" Aristotle immediately went on to ask an important question concerning the entity time, thus conceived: Is this a mental entity or could it exist independent of the mind?

> Whether if soul did not exist time would exist or not, is a question that may fairly be asked; for if there cannot be someone to count there cannot be anything that can be counted, so that evidently there cannot be number; for number is either what has been, or what can be, counted. But if nothing but soul, or in soul reason, is qualified to count, there would not be time unless there were soul, but only that of which time is an attribute, i.e. if movement can exist without soul, and the before and after are attributes of time, and time is these *qua* numerable.[33]

(Here we may read "measure" for "count" and "number.") It may be recalled that Aristotle's main argument for his definition of time, which entails that it is *not* independent of motion, was a phenomenological argument. Thus, the question of mind dependence arose at the very outset, as Aquinas pointed out.[34]

Aristotle's answer to this question is not entirely clear. The translation above suggests that in the absence of mind there would be no time, only movement. Aquinas, however, read this as a position that was considered but rejected by Aristotle. It is clear, however, that there is an important modal fallacy in the argument, as pointed out by Aquinas.

> But perhaps the conditional proposition which he gave first is true; that is, if it is impossible for there to be someone who numbers, then it is impossible for there to be anything numerable. . . . But it does

not follow that, if there is no one who numbers, then there is nothing numerable, as the Philosopher's objection proceeds.[35]

In a world in which there are no beings capable of measurement, a process might still have a certain duration (as compared to another process) in the sense that if there had been measuring beings, they could have ascertained this fact. This is the conclusion pointed to by Aquinas. (But this conclusion uses counterfactual notions, which are the subject of philosophical dispute even when no obvious fallacy is involved.)

The subsequent history of the question contains instances of all the possible positions that can be taken. Maimonides firmly maintained that time is dependent in its existence on the existence of motion, but not on anything else (including mind). Avicenna argued, however, that time does not exist except in the mind because the relations of before and after are constituted only by memory and expectation. Duns Scotus attempted a synthesis: Insofar as time is an aspect of movement it is independent of mind, because movement is; insofar as time is a measure, its existence is dependent on the existence of a being able to measure.[36] René Descartes and Benedict de Spinoza maintained that the distinction between movement and time is a distinction of reason alone and that time is only "a mode of thinking."[37] Barrow and Newton went to the opposite extreme; Leibniz, on the other hand, maintained that time was an ideal entity, and he appears to have a conceptualist position. A new synthesis was attempted by Immanuel Kant. We see here an almost paradigm example of the thesis-antithesis-synthesis dialectical movement in the history of philosophy. We shall now take a brief look at Kant's attempt to provide a synthesis of the positions of Leibniz and Newton, restricting our attention to natural philosophy and to Kant's early writings.

b. The Kantian Concept of Time

Leibniz, we recall, defined "time" as "the order of noncontemporaneous events." This is also a direct answer to the question "What is time?" Leibniz elaborated on it by saying that time was something, *an ideal entity*.[38] Newtonian absolute time would be a concrete entity, just as the earth, the

galaxy, and the fixed stars are concrete entities. Numbers, relations, and mathematical constructs are ideal entities. Corresponding to any collection of physical objects are such ideal
entities as its number and spatial configuration. Corresponding to any collection of events are such ideal entities as its number and its temporal order. When this collection comprises all
events, its temporal order is just time itself.

Leonhart Euler raised two main objections to this position.[39]
The first is that time has parts (the year 1748, the twentieth
century, and so on). But how can an order have parts? Note,
furthermore, that these parts are themselves ordered by the
familiar temporal relations (the year 1748 is before the twentieth century). Is time, then, also the order of the parts of
time—and if so, does this not lead to a vicious circle? The
second objection is that any conceived event is conceived of as
being located in time: time is the location not only of all actual
events but of all possible events. If time is simply the order of
all actual events, how can it provide a location for the merely
possible events? These objections made a great impression on
Kant, and he always considered them to have been correct,
although he did not remain a Newtonian.

Both Euler's objections are puzzling, despite their intuitive
appeal; and we shall do well to see how Leibniz might have
answered them. The first objection is the less difficult of the
two, because of the possibility of rephrasing all assertions
about the parts of time. For example, instead of saying "It
happened on such and such a day" we could say "It happened
during such and such a revolution of the earth," since the days
are marked by these revolutions. Even the Newtonians admit
that *we* can refer to, or describe, a specific part of time only
through reference to the events occurring in it. Second, all the
parts of time are indexed by coordinates (dates). Thus, para-
phrases in terms of these coordinates are also available. The
Newtonian might say that the time variable t of physics ranges
over absolute instants, but the Leibnizian can hold that t
ranges over the real numbers used as time coordinates. (He
would then have to show that the use of these coordinates does
not commit him to the existence of absolute instants, but he
has that task in any case.)

The second point, that possible events are to be conceived of
as located in time, Leibniz fully granted.

The void which can be conceived in time, indicates, like that in space, that time and space apply as well to possible as to existing things.

Time and space are of the nature of eternal truths which concern equally the possible and the existing.[40]

But precisely what is meant by this will be clear if we remember Leibniz's answer to Barrow's argument concerning the possibility of creation. Consider the two possible states of affairs.

England is separated from the Continent by a sea.
England is not separated from the Continent by a sea.

Of these one is actual, the other merely possible. According to Leibniz, this means that the one is the case in that possible world which is the actual world, and the other is the case in some other possible world. Certainly, both could not be located in the same possible world. That both must be conceived of as being located in time means that whichever world *is* actual, its states of affairs have a temporal order, and that is time. So if some other possible world is conceived of as actual, time is conceived to be the temporal order of *its* states; hence, those states are conceived of as being in time. (One might say: Each possible world has *its* time, and time simpliciter is the time of the actual world.)

Kant objected that this is not how we think of it; we do not think of time as possibly having been different from what it is, but only of the order of events or states *in* time as possibly having been different—and *mutatis mutandis* for space. Kant generalized this by saying that there is a certain general form that any possible world must have; a possible world is just this necessary general form filled out by certain contingent contents. Time and space are but aspects of this form. In his *Inaugural Dissertation*, he characterized this general form as "the principle of possible interactions":

. . . the bond constituting the *essential* form of a world is regarded as the principle of *possible interactions* of the substances constituting the world. For actual interactions do not belong to essence but to state.[41]

Later, Kant characterized this general form of the physical

(i.e., for him, phenomenal) world as being made necessary by the a priori principles of our understanding. These principles determine the structure of our conceptual scheme, and hence, how we conceive of the physical world. A similar position concerning the general form of any possible world appears in Wittgenstein's *Tractatus Logico-Philosophicus* (though Wittgenstein does not ask whether this general form is made necessary by principles governing our understanding).

> 2.013. Each thing is, as it were, in a space of possible states of affairs. This space I can imagine empty. But I cannot imagine the thing without the space.

> 2.0131. . . . A speck in the visual field, though it need not be red, must have some color: it is, so to speak, surrounded by colour-space. Tone must have *some* pitch, objects of the sense of touch *some* degree of hardness, and so on.

> 2.022. It is obvious that an imagined world, however different it may be from the real one, must have *something*—a form—in common with it.

> 2.0251. Space, time, and colour are forms of objects.

> 2.11. A picture presents a situation in logical space, the existence and non-existence of states of affairs.[42]

Thus, the assertion that something is of a certain kind entails that there is a set of families of properties such that this thing is characterized by one member of each family:

> X is a medium-large physical object *entails* that X is somewhere in space, has some color, some texture, some shape, and. . . . X is an event *entails* X is somewhere in time, and. . . .

The collection of these families of properties determines the *logical space* of that kind of thing. (Each family by itself, or each subcollection of these families, determines a subspace of that logical space, which may itself be called a logical space. Thus, Wittgenstein speaks of the "colour-space.")

As we indicated above, the critical philosophy developed by Kant turned questions of natural philosophy into questions concerning consciousness and the understanding. Thus, in the "Transcendental Aesthetic," time is characterized as "a necessary representation that underlies all intuitions" and as "a pure form of sensible intuition," "the subjective condition under which alone intuition can take place in us."[43] But if we remain on the level of natural philosophy—a shallow level of analysis for those who prefer to turn to a transcendental critique of our conceptual scheme—the foremost question is about the form of this pure form of intuition. The question "What is time?" requires us—if we accept its presupposition— to objectify this form of our intuition and to describe it as a form, as opposed to a condition of sensible perception. But this concern is more characteristic of the *Inaugural Dissertation,* and of the *Tractatus Logico-Philosophicus,* than of the *Critique of Pure Reason.*

Remaining, then, on the level of natural philosophy, we may sum up as follows: time is a logical space, a subspace of the total logical space of events. But what is a logical space? Wittgenstein gives the example of the color spectrum: the logical space of colored things. But what exactly is the color spectrum? It is merely a strip or line segment with markings, whether drawn on paper, merely imagined, or produced on a scale on the wall by means of a light source and prism. What it *does* is to give a picture, to a desired degree of accuracy, of the part of our conceptual scheme that concerns colors. ("Why can't a thing be red and green all over?" "Because 'red' and 'green' are the tags of different parts of the spectrum, and an evenly colored surface has a unique location on the spectrum.") To put it more generally: The color spectrum is a segment of the real line being used to represent the meaning relations among the color words.

A further point must be noted: The color spectrum also represents all possible relations among things with respect to color. Whether two colored patches match, for example, is uniquely determined by their location in the color spectrum. It has been suggested that the converse is also the case: what color a thing has is uniquely determined by what matching relations it bears to all other colored things. But then "all colored things" must be understood to refer to all such *possible* things. For surely it is conceivable that certain shades of color are not the color of any actual thing. In this sense, the color spectrum accommodates all possibilities; in Leibniz's phrase, it concerns "equally the possible and the existing."

Analogously, we can reconstruct the view that time is an ideal entity, but nevertheless an aspect of the form of any possible world, as meaning that time is a logical space pertaining to events. Its structure is to mirror our conceptual scheme insofar as it concerns temporal properties and relations. Here, the real line (taken either as a geometric or a number theoretic construct) suggests itself as being capable of this function. Thus, Kant writes:

> We represent the time-sequence by a line progressing to infinity, in which the manifold constitutes a series of one dimension only; and we reason from the properties of this line to all the properties of time. . . .[44]

In other words, the position we are presently discussing is that time is a logical space and that a logical space is, in general, a mathematical construct used to represent conceptual interconnections among a family of properties and relations—and furthermore, that this logical space (time) is the real line being used to represent all possible temporal relations among events and the conceptual interconnections among these relations. (Thus, simultaneity is represented by identity of location on the real line, and the fact that temporal precedence is incompatible with simultaneity is reflected by the incompatibility of $<$ and $=$.)[45]

Clear appreciation of this view is found in the philosophy of science developed by the Neo-Kantian school. In a section entitled "Die Zeit als mathematische Gebilde," Paul Natorp writes:

> If one considers time as it appears in the basic science of nature—the pure theory of motion, or mechanics—one finds it represented there as a fixed, unchanging, unique ordering, in which all natural objects must, as it were, take their place and which they must run through. . . . According to this conception, the temporal order coincides exactly—insofar as its mathematical properties are concerned—with the one-dimensional, straight, sequential ordering of the *numbers*.

In all respects, time appears as the real line in the equations of motion of mechanics and in the whole of physics.[46]

In other words, the customary formulation of Newtonian mechanics presupposes that temporal relations among events can be represented by the relations on the real line. The use of the time variable t in physics, which ranges over the real-number continuum, is based on an assumed isomorphism between the system of temporal relations among events and a system of relations on this continuum.

But of course, the real line cannot be used to represent the totality of temporal relations adequately, unless this isomorphism really exists. Here we have a significant objection to the position that time is the logical space that we have just seen described. For we recall that the theory of closed time, which must certainly be taken seriously as a conceptual alternative, leads to the conclusion that this isomorphism does not exist. It leads to the conclusion that not the real line but a topologically closed curve (or the extended real-number system) is needed to represent the system of temporal relations. This certainly shows that the position we have extracted from the writing of Kant, Natorp, and Wittgenstein is too narrow.

This is, no doubt, due to the presumption that we can a priori determine the structure that time *must* have or a necessary form that any possible world must have. If the necessary principles determining the form of the world are not vacuous tautologies, then we can conceive their violation—and what, then, is the basis of their necessity? The answer of the Critical Philosophy is, of course, that the transcendental method may ferret out synthetic (nontautological) and yet a priori necessary conditions for the possibility of any experience or coherent thought of the world. Today, there is basic agreement among most if not all philosophers that a transcendental proof of this sort is after all not feasible. Such agreement does not establish that the proof is not feasible; according to the rationale of inquiry, however, the final lack of success of the Critical method is good reason to explore its alternatives.

On the other hand, there is much that is valuable in the Kantian position. In Section 7c we shall try to show in what sense it is still possible (and illuminating) to regard time as a logical space.

c. Time as a Logical Space, and the Structure of Events

We characterize the notion of *logical space* by saying that a logical space is a certain mathematical construct used to represent certain conceptual interconnections. By representing real things (instances of those concepts) by means of elements of this mathematical construct (their "locations") we also represent relations among those things. The notion of logical space plays an important role elsewhere in philosophy of science, and also in philosophy of logic, and it seems worthwhile to inquire further into how time might be considered a logical space.

If we do consider time, then we must distinguish clearly between the total relational structure of events that is world history, and time. Even if we use only the temporal relations to define the former structure, it will not be time. Rather, it is a structure that is presumed to be adequately represented by our logical space. This does not mean that our logical space must be a mathematical construct isomorphic to the actual temporal structure of events. It is necessary only that the latter can be embedded in the former. Thus, the totality of all colored things and the color relations (of matching, contrasting, and so on) among them probably do not yield a structure isomorphic to the color spectrum. Such isomorphism obtains only if for every color on the spectrum there is a colored object that has this color.

Should we then say that the logical space must be such that the corresponding real structure must necessarily be embeddable in it? The answer can be given only through a distinction concerning the concept of *necessity*. If what is intended here is logical necessity, the answer ought to be negative. For we are concerned with the idea of time as it appears in our common conceptual framework and in the conceptual framework of the physical sciences. There can be no guarantee—and here we differ emphatically with Kant—that any conceptual scheme or theory must be such that the actual world fits it. If this turns out not to be so, then we hope eventually to change our theories for the better. But the possible change in theory that our dialogue with the world may eventually occasion cannot be foreseen; its only bounds are those of logical consistency and necessity. Therefore, our task as philosophers of science *cannot* be to elaborate a framework within which the scientist can remain no matter what the vicissitudes of experimental evidence. On such a subject, our position could be tenable only if it were trivial. Our task is, rather, to elucidate and further to articulate the conceptual scheme of accepted scientific theories. (And since we are presently concerned only with the macrophysical world, that means classical and relativistic physics.)

So to the above question we must answer: Yes, the actual temporal structure of events must necessarily be embeddable in our logical space. But necessity here must be construed not as absolute logical necessity but as necessity relativized to the scientific theories that we accept.

Here, however, we must consider a serious challenge: Why should we not content ourselves to describe the actual structure of events insofar as such a description is possible on the basis of accepted theories? And why should *that* structure not be called "time"? Indeed, there is a good precedent for this. Russell's theory of time proceeded in exactly this manner: *Time* is the series of instants, and *instant* is defined in terms of the notions *event,* *(temporally) overlaps,* and *(temporally wholly) precedes.*[47] The definitions are as follows:

X is an *instant: X* is an exhaustive class of mutually overlapping events.

Event *E* is *at* instant *X: E* is a member of *X.*

Instant *X* is *before* instant *Y:* some member of *X* (wholly) precedes some member of *Y.*

Will the series of instants thus defined have any of the properties we wish to ascribe to time? Not necessarily; but this just means that we might find out that the structure of world history is not as we have heretofore conceived it. To ensure that the appropriate kind of series has been defined we must introduce some empirical assumptions about events to the effect that there are "enough" events distributed "randomly enough" with respect to the temporal relations. For example, to secure the conclusion that no instant has a next instant (just as there is no rational number next to 1/2), Russell assumes:

> It is impossible for an event to cease just before another begins (in the sense that if E covers a stretch of time just before E', there must be an instant X such that both E and E' are at X).

"Whether this is the case or not," Russell writes, "is an empirical question; but if it is not, there is no reason to expect the time series to be compact."[48]

This certainly presents a challenge to the position that time is a logical space. However, it is not really a challenge of the sort provided by an alternative answer to the same question ("What is time?"). Events are located in time, and the structure of world history is set in time, and we conceive world history to be set in this same time regardless of the form it actually takes. This is, of course, the Kantian objection to Leibniz's theory. To say that time is the actual structure of world history is really to say that our concept of time (as opposed to our concept of world history) is mistaken or superfluous. This is a perfectly possible position, but it is the position that "What is time?" is a question mistaken in intent. Only confusion can result if we say: Yes, time exists, but it is really the actual temporal structure of the totality of events; it was a mistake to conceive of the latter as simply one of many possible such structures *in* time.

Our conclusion is that it is not necessary to say that there is such a thing as time, but that if we do, the best possible answer to the further question what kind of thing it is, is that it is a logical space. First, this notion has sufficient flexibility to escape the criticism of the Kantian position that it is too narrow. For in answer to the development of physical science, we might take as our logical space the real line, or some segment of the real line, or the extended real-number system. This change would have been made definitively if in an accepted cosmological theory the time variable t came to range not over the real-number continuum but over one of these other mathematical structures. Then, we would say that time has a beginning or time is topologically closed. Now we say that the possibility that time has a beginning or that time is topologically closed cannot be ruled out, because we see that physical science might lead to such a conception of actual world structure that we might make the corresponding conceptual transition.[49] The necessity, which Kant perceived, of time having the structure of the real line is only the necessity of a conceptual scheme that developed with the success of Newtonian physics. But this necessity is still with us in the sense that we have not accepted an alternative; only, recent cosmological speculation, and the violent demise of the classical framework (in some important respects) have greatly increased our tolerance of ambiguity at this point.

Finally, the view that time is a logical space allows a "Scotist" synthesis on the question whether time is a mind-dependent entity. A logical space is a mathematical construct *used to represent . . .*; and that means, of course, *used by us.* If we users and representators did not exist, neither would there be something being used to represent. The real line cannot be used to represent the actual temporal structure of events unless the latter can be embedded in it. This is purely and entirely an objective question of empirical fact. But neither can the real line thus be used unless there are those capable of using it. Hence, in that case the logical space *time* (which is something used to represent something else) could not then exist.

But this sense in which there would be no time were there no beings capable of reason, is innocuous. It is the sense in which there would be no food were there no organisms, and no teacups if there were no tea drinkers.[50] There could be things that look like what, in our world, teacups look like. There could be things that could be used to drink tea from (buckets, shells, and so on). But teacups are the things that *we* use to drink tea, and in that sense they are as much a cultural object as chess or the Polonaise.

Chapter *IV*

The Classical
Problems
of the
Theory of
Space

In this chapter we address philosophical problems concerning space that arose before the advent of the theory of relativity. In some respects, these problems roughly parallel those of the theory of time; to stave off boredom we shall concentrate on those aspects that are peculiar to space.

1. The Absolute and the
Relational Theory of Space

a. The Views of Newton and Leibniz

In the *Scholium* to the definitions in his *Principia,* Newton introduced the concept of absolute space, in which "all things are placed . . . as to order of situation." "Absolute space," Newton writes, "in its own nature, without relation to anything external, remains always similar and immovable."[1] Newton's position became enormously influential, as did his theory of absolute time; one of his followers, John Keill, summarized the conception aptly as follows:

> We conceive Space to be that, wherein all Bodies are placed . . .; that it is altogether penetrable, receiving all Bodies into itself, and refusing Ingress to nothing whatsoever; that it is immovably fixed, capable of no Action, Form, or Quality; whose Parts it is impossible to separate from each other, by any Force however great; but the Space itself remaining immovable, receives the Successions of things in motion, determines the Velocities of their Motions, and measures the Distances of the things themselves.[2]

Thus, Newtonians explain their concept of space by saying that space is very much like a material body, of a very ethereal kind, but not entirely. The main disanalogy—that bodies are in space but that it is nonsense to ask where space is—they do not grant: parts of space "are, as it were, the places of themselves as well as of all other things."[3]

Leibniz's conception of space as relational, that is, as not itself a concrete entity, is opposed to this. Newton grants, of course, that motion can be relative, that is, the distance (or some other spatial relation) between bodies may change with time; this we call motion. But Newton holds, and Leibniz denies, that when that happens, at least one of the bodies is in absolute motion, that is, motion relative to space itself. Leibniz's most famous statements of his position are found in his fifth letter to Clarke.

> 47. I will here show how men come to form to themselves the notion of space. They consider that many things exist at once and they observe in them a certain order of co-existence, according to which the relation of one thing to another is more or less simple. This order, is their *situation* or distance. When it happens that one of those co-existent things changes its relation to a multitude of others, which do not change their relation among themselves; and that another thing, newly come, acquires the same relation to the others, as the former had; we then say it is come into the place of the former. . . . And supposing, or feigning, that among those co-existents, there is a sufficient number of them, which have undergone no change; then we may say, that those which have such a relation to those fixed exist-

ents, as others had to them before, have now the *same place* which those others had. And that which comprehends all those places, is called *space*.[4]

The phrase "that which comprehends" is of course not too perspicuous, but Leibniz makes it quite clear with an analogy to genealogical structure:

> In like manner, as the mind can fancy to itself an order made up of genealogical lines, whose bigness would consist only in the number of generations, wherein every person would have his place: and if to this one should add the fiction of a *metempsychosis,* and bring in the human souls again; the persons in those lines might change place; he who was a father, or a grandfather, might become a son, or a grandson, etc. And yet those genealogical places, lines, and spaces, though they should express real truth, would only be ideal things.[5]

No one, of course, would suggest that there exists an absolute genealogical space in which persons are placed as to order of kinship, except in the sense that the kinship relations define a certain mathematical structure. But Newton holds that the case of space proper is quite different, and we shall now examine his arguments to support this view.

b. Newton's Arguments for Absolute Space

Newton's term "absolute motion" refers, by definition, to motion relative to absolute space. Hence, if Newton can establish that there is absolute motion, then we must grant him that there is absolute space. This provides Newton with his basic strategy, summarized by him as follows:

> It is indeed a matter of great difficulty to discover and effectually to distinguish the true motions of particular bodies from the apparent. . . . Yet the thing is not altogether desperate; for we have some arguments to guide us, partly from the apparent motions, which are the differences of true motions; partly from the forces which are the causes and effects of the true motions. . . .[6]

What can Newton possibly have meant by arguments "from the apparent motions, which are the differences of true motions"? If A and B are in relative motion with respect to each other, then there can be nothing with respect to which both A and B are at rest. But from this we certainly cannot conclude that either A or B is then in motion with respect to absolute space, unless we first assume that absolute space exists. Certainly, within Newton's theory the conclusion follows, but only via the principle that is in dispute here.

The arguments "from the forces which are the causes and effects of the true motions" concern accelerated motion. For Newton's laws say that a body not subject to forces persists in whatever state of motion (uniform, rectilinear) it has, but that (absolute) accelerations are caused by forces. Thus, the second argument is apparently that if two bodies accelerate relative to each other, this is caused by a force acting on at least one of the bodies and that body is also accelerating relative to absolute space.

The question here is what the status is of the assertion "Absolute acceleration is caused by a force." Leibniz failed entirely to see any cogency in this argument because of his different evaluation of the status of that principle. For him, it was an assertion in Newtonian terms of a fact that could be stated, insofar as it had any empirical relevance, also in his terms. In his fifth letter to Clarke, Leibniz grants that if two bodies are in relative accelerated motion, this is caused by a force, and that we may be able to distinguish by measurement the body on which this force is impressed.

> I find nothing in . . . the Scholium . . . that proves, or can prove, the reality of space in itself. However, I grant there is a difference between an absolute true motion of a body, and a mere relative change of its situation with respect to another body. For when the immediate cause of the change is in the body, that body is truly in motion. . . .[7]

Later commentators suggest that this admission is fatal to Leibniz's case, because, after all, if there is absolute true motion then there is absolute space. But Leibniz explains here very clearly that what he means by true motion is not what Newton means by absolute motion. By "X is in true motion" Leibniz means that X is in some relative motion, which is caused by a force impressed on X. How could we tell that the force is acting on *X* rather than on some other body? This leads us to Newton's last argument.

When a body is truly accelerating, this is accompanied by certain *force effects*. If a driver accelerates his car, he feels the effect in his stomach and shoulders; if a coin is placed on a smooth rotating disc, it is flung off; if a pail full of water is made to rotate, the surface of the water becomes hollow. This last example, of the centrifugal-force effects accompanying rotation, is Newton's. Moreover, he gives the following example:

> . . . if two globes, kept at a given distance one from the other by means of a cord that connects them, were revolved about their common centre of gravity, we might, from the tension of the cord, discover the endeavor of the globes to recede from the axis of their motion, and from thence . . . compute the quantity of their circular motions.[8]

So Newton explains that we can detect absolute rotation by detecting centrifugal forces—and in general, absolute acceleration by accelerative forces. How would Leibniz analyze Newton's argument? For him, it would have the following structure:

(1) Absolute motion is motion relative to absolute space. (Definition)
(2) True motion is motion caused by a force on the body in question. (Definition)
(3) Centrifugal-force effects imply the existence of a force that is causing rotational motion.
(4) Centrifugal-force effects imply true rotational motion. (From [2] and [3])
(5) A body is in true motion if and only if it is in absolute motion. (A principle of Newton's theory)
(6) Hence, centrifugal-force effects imply absolute motion.

Leibniz accepts (3) as correct, *ordinarily* (the qualification will be discussed below). And he would grant that the argument above is valid. But the most important premise, (5), Leibniz does not grant. And certainly, Newton has given no explicit reason why (5) should be accepted.

We qualified Leibniz's acceptance of (3) by the term "ordinarily." The reason for this is that in this connection, the Newtonians liked to talk of an extraordinary case, the case in which the system exhibiting the force effects is alone in the universe. With reference to the example of the globes, Newton says: "And thus we might find the quantity . . . of this circular motion, even in an immense vacuum, where there was nothing external or sensible with which the globes could be compared." This is very important, for the spatial relations between the two globes do not change; hence, if there is nothing else, the situation involves no change of spatial relations at all. If it still involves motion, then it follows that motion is not essentially a change of spatial relations.

Here the Leibnizian has a dilemma. He can say that (3) holds only if there is something to be moved relative to, to put it colloquially. Or he can deny that in the absence of other bodies the globes would exhibit any force effects.

For Leibniz, force was such a basic notion and so clearly independent of all spatial and kinematic notions that it seems most plausible that he would have chosen the first alternative.[9] This alternative was first fully elaborated by George Berkeley. In his *Principles of Human Knowledge* (1710) he made clear the exact distinction we draw between true and absolute motion. In his *De Motu* (1721) he clearly explains what we here call the "first alternative":

> 59. Then let two globes be conceived to exist and nothing corporeal besides them. Let forces then be conceived to be applied in some way; whatever we may understand by the application of forces, a circular motion of the two globes round a common centre cannot be conceived. . . .[10]

Thus, if with Leibniz we grant the reality of forces, then we would have to say only that centrifugal forces cause (1) the familiar force effects, such as the tension in the cord joining the globes; and (2) change of spatial relations with respect to other bodies, not similarly affected, *if any*.

A more up-to-date Newtonian might argue that if such effects occurred in the absence of other bodies, then Newton's theory puts us in a position to explain their occurrence, through the hypothesis of absolute motion. But for Newton himself, forces were causes of motions, tensions, and deformations, and motions were not the causes of any of these other phenomena. Hence, Newton could not have offered the fact of motion as explaining the effects, but only as suggesting an explanation in terms of force, via the principle that accelerations only occur when there are forces present. Berkeley disagreed with both Leibniz and Newton; he regarded the notion of force as merely a technical or conceptual device. So for him rotations and centrifugal effects always accompany each other —as a brute fact of common experience—and no conclusion whatever can be drawn about what would happen if the world were very different than it is.

Almost 200 years later, Ernst Mach elaborated both this Berkeleian view of forces and what we have called the "second alternative"—that is, he simply denied that the effects that accompany acceleration in our experience would occur in the absence of other bodies.[11] It is easy to see, however, that either alternative provides a way out of Newton's argument. Hence, neither need be embraced *in toto* by the Leibnizian. He may answer the Newtonian simply: Force effects may not occur at all in the absence of other bodies, but if they do our physics is not weakened in any way by holding that they can indicate motion only if there are other bodies; in fact, this will follow from the definition of motion as change of spatial relations among bodies.

c. The Relational Theory of Space and the Laws of Motion

From our present vantage point, it is easy to underestimate the enormous influence of Newton's mechanics on the eighteenth and nineteenth centuries. The laws of motion were stated in terms of absolute space; moreover, they were true and perhaps necessarily true; therefore, the theory of absolute space must be true. This is, essentially, the argument propounded in Euler's *Réflexions sur l'espace et le temps*.[12]

The weak link here is obviously the premise that the laws of motion, as stated, are true. An opponent such as Leibniz or Berkeley need not disagree with Newton on any experimentally verifiable assertion. The evidence for the laws of motion could only be that they "save the phenomena," that is, they agree with the experimental facts.

That absolute space is in some sense not the direct object of any observation Newton granted without reserve. For this reason, he had to introduce the notion of a relative space, or, as we would now say, a frame of reference:

> But because the parts of space cannot be seen, or distinguished from one another by our senses, therefore in their stead we use sensible measures of them. For from the positions and distances of things from any body considered as immovable, we define all places; and then, with respect to such places, we estimate all motions, considering bodies as transferred from some of those places into others. And so, instead of absolute places and motions, we use relative ones. . . .[13]

Of course, absolute space coincides with one of these (possible) relative spaces—but which one? To answer this question we must be able to find a body absolutely at rest. Whereas absolute accelerated motion can, according to Newton, be distinguished experimentally from absolute unaccelerated motion, however, the latter cannot thus be distinguished from absolute rest.[14]

It seemed clear already in Newton's time that the fixed stars provide a reference system that is experimentally indistinguishable from that of absolute space. These frames are called *inertial* frames, a notion apparently not systematically elaborated until the end of nineteenth century.[15] Hence, what was more natural for Newton's opponents to suggest than that the notion of absolute space may be replaced everywhere in mechanics by that of the frame of reference of the fixed stars? One drawback is that further experimental evidence might show, for example, centrifugal forces in bodies not rotating relative to the fixed stars. But that is only a practical difficulty; to accommodate the new evidence a new frame of reference might be chosen in which the fixed stars move ever so slightly. All an opponent of Newton needs is some frame of reference that can take the place of absolute space in mechanics. To this argument Euler brought an objection of principle:

> If they say that it is with respect to the fixed stars that the principle of inertia must be explained, it would be very difficult to refute them since the fixed stars . . . are so far from us. But it will be a very

strange principle of metaphysics and contrary to others of its dogmas to say that the fixed stars direct bodies in their inertia.[16]

In other words, if we replace the notion of absolute space by that of the frame of reference of the fixed stars, we shall explain the occurrence of centrifugal-force effects by the fact of rotation relative to the fixed stars. But how could the stars cause these effects?

This argument is altogether unfair. Leibniz would attribute both the rotation relative to the fixed stars and the centrifugal-force effects, to a force acting on the body, just as Newton would. True, Berkeley (and later, Mach) would not postulate such forces, but neither are they compelled to postulate a causal efficacy in the fixed stars. The argument to which Euler is objecting is entirely general with respect to inertial frames and involves no empirical hypotheses at all.

We may give Euler's objection a slightly different form by saying that Newton's opponents must give to inertial frames the privileged role that Newton gave to absolute space. Just what would explain this privileged status of the inertial frames of reference among all the possible frames of reference?

The answer is that, essentially, the inertial frames do not have a privileged status at all. The laws of motion are a set of statements about mass, motion, and force; therefore, they will be true in some frames of reference, in none, or in all. As it happens, they are true in some frames; these we call the inertial frames. We find Newton's laws of interest because they are approximated in some frames of reference that are of interest to us (because they are relatively easy to identify: the earth, the sun, the fixed stars). The aim to have a physical theory in which the laws hold for every frame of reference has been a major motivation in the development of the theory of relativity; and this aim has often been portrayed as the development of a new philosophical basis for the theory of space in physics. But it is misleading to think of the relation between physics and philosophy in such simple terms. Specifically, the fact that the laws of a given theory hold only in some frames of reference can, as such, imply nothing about the status of these frames in nature.

2. The Development of Modern Geometry

a. Euclidean Geometry

Since antiquity, the ideal of a rigorous science has been that of an axiomatic system, and this has been due in no small measure to the fact that Euclid had succeeded in developing geometry axiomatically. Indeed, philosophers were wont to speak of the axiomatic method as that of an exposition *more geometrico*.

Euclid's *Elements* begins with the introduction of the basic terms of geometry. It is true that he attempted to define each of these in more familiar terms, but that is helpful only in that it gives the reader an intuitive guide to their use. Next, Euclid lists the basic principles of the discipline; here, he draws a distinction (no longer in use) between *axioms* and *postulates*. The axioms are principles that concern "common notions," that is, notions not peculiar to geometry. Specifically, the axioms concern the notion of magnitude, and say, for example, that equality is transitive (If $x = y$ and $y = z$, then $x = z$) and is preserved by the addition of equals (If $x = y$ and $z = w$, then $x + z = y + w$).

The postulates concern distinctively geometric notions. There are five, and in modern idiom* they may be stated as follows:

(I) If x and y are distinct points, there is a straight line incident with both.

(II) Any finite straight line (segment) is part of a unique infinite straight line.

(III) If x is a point and r a finite distance, there is a unique circle with x and radius r.

(IV) Any two right angles are equal.

(V) If a straight line falling on two straight lines makes

---

* I.e., with some modern improvements, eliminating ambiguities. The fifth postulate has been left as nearly in Euclid's phrasing as possible, however.

the interior angles on the same side less than two
right angles, the two straight lines, if produced in-
definitely, meet on that side on which the angles are
less than two right angles.

Note that we now usually say "line segment" rather than
"finite line," reserving the word "line" for something infinite.
If we adopt this policy, then postulates (I) and (II) say that on
any two distinct points there is a unique straight line. Assumptions now usually made explicit include, for example,
that each line segment contains at least two points and that
when two lines meet, they meet in a point. Then it follows
from postulates (I) and (II) that two lines cannot meet in more
than one point; hence, they cannot enclose an area.

To understand postulate (IV) we must note that Euclid
thought of geometric figures as movable; he considered them
equal ("congruent") if they could be placed in complete coincidence with each other. There is clearly a presupposition
here (of which postulate [IV] is meant to guarantee the truth)—
namely, that if two figures can be brought into coincidence
in one position, this is also possible in any other position.
This assumption was first made wholly explicit by Hermann
von Helmholtz and became known as the *principle of free mobility* (we shall discuss this in more detail in Section 2d).

The fifth postulate has a long and interesting history, which
seems to have been due largely to the prevalent view that
postulates ought to be self-evident principles. Apparently,
the first four postulates seemed self-evident to everyone, and
the fifth did not. To allay the doubts, there were many attempts to prove that it followed, in fact, from the first four
postulates, and therefore did not need to be self-evident. It is
rather difficult to see how the fifth postulate came to be
thought of in such different terms from the others. One sug-
gestion is that the fifth postulate is less intuitive, because if the
sum of the interior angles is very little less than two right
angles, the meeting point is so distant that our intuition ceases
to guide us. After all, it is argued, any area comprised in direct experience is relatively small; extrapolation from experience beyond such relatively small areas must therefore be
risky. But this argument will not do; the other postulates go

beyond experience in just the same way. If that were the explanation, why no doubts about the uniqueness of an infinite line containing a given finite segment? or about circles with arbitrarily great radii?

Whatever the explanation, it remained a great comfort that Euclid was able to deduce from postulates (I) to (IV) the result that if the interior angles do equal two right angles in sum, then the lines are parallel (i.e., they do not intersect). So if *l* is a line and *x* a point not on *l*, then there is at least one line *l'* through *x* that is parallel to *l*. But is there more than one? The most famous attempt to produce a negative answer is that of the Italian priest Girolamo Saccheri, in his work *Euclides ab omni naevo vindicatus . . . (Euclid cleansed of all blemish . . .)* published in 1733. Ironically, Saccheri's attempt is famous because it comes so near to showing that the fifth postulate cannot be deduced from the first four. Saccheri investigated the possibility that more than one parallel to *l* can be drawn through a point not on *l*. He called this the *acute-angle hypothesis,* and although he tried, he could deduce no explicit contradiction from it. But its consequences were so strange to him that he concluded that "the hypothesis of acute angle is absolutely false; because repugnant to the nature of the straight line."[17] At the beginning of the nineteenth century, several mathematicians were willing to take this repugnancy in stride, and non-Euclidean geometry was developed.

b. Non-Euclidean Geometry

The part of Euclidean geometry not dependent on the fifth postulate came to be called *absolute geometry*. This is the part that follows from postulates (I) to (IV), and it comprises specifically the first twenty-eight theorems. By adding postulate (V), absolute geometry is extended into Euclidean geometry. By adding a denial of postulate (V), it can be extended into *hyperbolic geometry*.

Hyperbolic geometry, the first non-Euclidean geometry, was developed independently by Karl Friedrich Gauss, János Bolyai, and Nikolai Lobachevsky in the early nineteenth century. The specific alternative of the fifth postulate that it employs is

(V*)   Through a point *x* not on a line *l*, there is more than one parallel to *l*.

If the words "more than" are omitted, we have an equivalent to the fifth postulate, as we saw in Section 2a.

Prominent among the theorems of absolute geometry is Euclid's theorem 17:

The sum of any two angles of a triangle is less than two right angles.

Clearly, the fifth postulate adds to this: And if the two base angles of a three-sided figure have a sum less than two right angles, the figure is a triangle. One can then prove that the sum of all three angles in the triangle is exactly that of two right angles. In hyperbolic geometry, the corresponding theorem is that in any triangle the sum of the angles is properly less than that of two right angles.

The term "absolute geometry" was somewhat ill chosen, for not very long after the development of hyperbolic geometry, Bernhard Riemann developed a geometry that also conflicts with absolute geometry. This geometry was called *spherical geometry;* and it rejects postulate (II) as well as postulate (V). The specific variant of postulate (V) that it employs is

(V**)   There is no line parallel to any other line.

From our discussion of postulate (II), however, it will be remembered that we now have a further choice. Shall the intersection of two lines be unique? For spherical geometry, postulate (II) is replaced by

(II*)   Any two lines have two distinct points in common.

Elliptical geometry, on the other hand, supplements postulate (V**) with

(II**)   Any two lines have a unique intersection.

Finally, Sophus Lie proved that in metric geometry, only four geometries are consistent with the principle of free mobility: Euclidean, hyperbolic, spherical, and elliptical.

The rise of non-Euclidean geometry marks also the advent of *metamathematics:* the study of properties of axiom systems, such as consistency. After all, that no contradictions were found in the development of the non-Euclidean geometries was no guarantee that there really were none. The first significant contribution to the subject was made by Eugenio Beltrami (1868), who gave an interpretation of hyperbolic geometry in Euclidean geometry. The importance of this is that any inconsistency in hyperbolic geometry would also show up in Euclidean geometry. Hence, if Euclidean geometry is consistent, so is hyperbolic geometry.

Beltrami singled out a certain kind of surface in Euclidean space and showed that the theorems of hyperbolic geometry can be interpreted as true statements concerning such surfaces. Somewhat later Poincaré simplified Beltrami's work a good deal, and we shall briefly describe Poincaré's version of the consistency proof for hyperbolic geometry.[18]

Let the line *l* separate a Euclidean plane into two parts: a lower part and an upper part. Let us call the points in the upper part (which does *not* contain *l*) the *U-points.* The *U-lines* will be the *upper halves* of lines perpendicular to *l* and of circles whose centers lie on *l*. Now distance is redefined in such a way that any point on *l* is infinitely far from any *U*-point. By this new metric, then, each *U*-line is infinitely long. In fact, all the postulates of absolute geometry are satisfied, if we take the points and lines to be exactly the *U*-points and *U*-lines. In addition, through each *U*-point *x* outside a *U*-line *l'* we can draw more than one *U*-line that does not intersect it in any *U*-point. Thus, the specific alternative to the fifth postulate that characterizes hyperbolic geometry is also satisfied.

The consistency proof for spherical geometry is simpler. Here, the model is a Euclidean sphere, the model's points being simply the points on the surface of the sphere, and the model's lines being the great circles on that sphere. Finally, a model for elliptic geometry is found by redefining distance on this sphere in such a way that spherically diametrical points are identified.[19]

c. Geometric Transformations and Coordinates

In Euclidean as well as non-Euclidean geometry, we are concerned with both order and metric relations: we speak of one point x lying between two other points y and z, but also of the distance $\overline{xy}$ between x and y. Other geometric notions are not as easy to classify. For example, with "line" we mean "straight line": lines are to be distinguished from other curves. Does this distinction belong to the subject of a geometric order or can it be made only in terms of the shortest distance between two points?

In the nineteenth century, a whole series of geometries was developed, which is more basic than Euclidean geometry because it involves fewer basic concepts. Thus, in *affine geometry,* the notions of distance and perpendicularity do not appear, in *projective geometry* neither these nor parallelism appears, and in *topology* (*analysis situs*) even the notion of line does not appear.

We have here the notion of one geometry being more basic than another in the sense that it involves fewer, more basic, concepts. How can these be constructed? What is the criterion according to which one family of geometric properties and relations is more basic than another such family? The answer was provided by a new approach to geometry initiated by Felix Klein in 1872.

Klein suggested that Euclidean geometry treats only certain properties of geometric figures as relevant or essential and regards all other properties as somehow irrelevant. For example, if we have a triangle and turn it upside down, any property of it that is changed by this operation is not a property dealt with in Euclidean geometry. One such inessential property would be "its vertex is 3 meters above sealevel." Another such property would be "its center is 3 millimeters east of its vertex." There are, of course, many other properties a figure may have that are equally inessential from the point of view of Euclidean geometry. Thus, whatever properties change when a figure is transposed from a green blackboard to a black blackboard, or to paper, are inessential. But if we flatten out an equilateral triangle in such a way that its vertex angle becomes greater than 90°, the transformation is not considered inessential in Euclidean geometry.

Klein's proposal was that each geometry G is characterized by a unique family T of transformations and deals with exactly those properties and relationships that are not changed by these transformations (in mathematical jargon: that are invariant under these transformations). And we may call G_1 more basic than G_2 if the family T_1 is a proper part of the family T_2.

We can now answer the questions that led us to this subject. Projective geometry is more basic than topology, and affine geometry is more basic than Euclidean but less basic than projective geometry. The associated families of transformations may be roughly characterized as follows:

> *Topological transformations* leave invariant the property of being a continuous region.
> *Projective transformations* are topological transformations and leave invariant the property of being a line and the relation of pair separation on a line.
> *Affine transformations* are projective transformations and leave invariant the relation of being parallel.
> *Euclidean transformations* are affine transformations and leave distances invariant.

Hyperbolic geometry may also be presented as subgeometry of projective geometry,[20] but we shall not go into this now. Instead, we turn to the analytic presentation of geometry, in which the notion of transformation can be given a precise meaning.

Let us begin by assuming as basic concepts those of *continuous region* and *line*. This takes us beyond topology, but not beyond projective geometry. We note that both continuous regions and lines are classes of points, and that we can talk of classes, and parts of classes, without introducing any geometric notions at all. We are now going to define order on a line, in two steps. Since we do not want to exclude spherical geometry, in which all lines are closed, the order relation on which we concentrate is that of pair separation.*

---

* In projective geometry, lines are also closed; the transition to affine geometry is effected by calling certain points "ideal" or "at infinity"; parallel lines can then "intersect at infinity." (Recall the use of a line "at infinity" in Poincaré's consistency proof for hyperbolic geometry.)

Definition: A *segment* of a line is any part of a line that it has in common with a continuous region.

Definition: If points x, y, z, and w are on line l, then $S(x, y/z, w)$ on l if and only if every segment of l that contains both x and y also contains either z or w.

We may postulate that S has all the properties definitive of the pair-separation relation—which indeed it will, if "line" and "continuous region" are given their usual geometric sense (see Chapter III, Section 1d).

If space is only one-dimensional, the assignment of coordinates is now easy. For then space is itself just a line, and we can define a coordinate assignment to be an assignment of elements of the extended real-number system in such a way that pair separation is reflected in a negative cross ratio.

If the line is open, the between relation is not vacuous:

Definition: Point x is *between* z and w on l if and only if every segment of l that contains z and w also contains x.

In that case, a coordinate assignment must simply assign real numbers to all the points in such a way that numerical betweenness among the coordinates reflects the defined betweenness relation among the points.

If the space is two-dimensional, the case is somewhat more complex. For simplicity, we shall suppose all the lines to be open. We shall not suppose however, that they are straight lines or that we have a notion of parallelism. There are still several ways in which to proceed, and we may choose one that is perhaps the most intuitive.

We begin by choosing two families of lines, F and G, such that

(a) If l is in F, it does not intersect any member of F, but does intersect each member of G (in a unique point).
(b) If l is in G, it does not intersect any member of G, but does intersect each member of F.
(c) Each point is the intersection of one line in F with one line in G.

The two families form a *grid*. We now choose one line in F and call it the X-axis, and one line in G, the Y-axis. The points on each of these axes are assigned real numbers in just the way that a one-dimensional space is coordinatized. Let us stipulate that the intersection of the X-axis and the Y-axis receives the number zero in both cases. We now assign each point p a pair (x, y) of coordinates as follows:

(d) The line in G that lies on p intersects the X-axis in the point that received x;
(e) The line in F that lies on p intersects the Y-axis in the point that received y.

If we wish to coordinatize a three-dimensional space, we must of course use three families, F, G, and H, and assign triples of coordinates. (Note that the assumption of the existence of a grid is nontrivial.)

At this point we can make the notion of transformation precise in two distinct but equivalent ways. This equivalence is very important, because for some problems the first point of view is natural, whereas for others the second point of view is appropriate.

(1) A transformation is a mapping t of each point p into a unique point $t(p)$. For example, if t is an affine transformation and the line on p and q is parallel to the line on p' and q', then the line on $t(p)$ and $t(q)$ is parallel to the line on $t(p')$ and $t(q')$.
(2) A transformation is a mapping t of each triple of coordinates (x,y,z) into a unique triple of coordinates $t(x,y,z) = (x',y',z')$. For example, if t is a Euclidean transformation, then the distance between (x_1,y_1,z_1) and (x_2,y_2,z_2), defined in the usual way, is the same as the distance between (x_1',y_1',z_1') *and* (x_2',y_2',z_2').

Thus, from the first point of view, a transformation moves the points around; it moves p into the place formerly occupied by $t(p)$, $t(p)$ into the place formerly occupied by $t(t(p))$, and so on. From the second point of view, the points are not being moved at all; they are just being assigned new coordinates. (In that case, we speak of a change in the frame of reference: the situation has not changed, but our point of view has.)

Of course, in case (1) we could instead say: There is really no motion involved; *p* just receives as new coordinates those that formerly belonged to *t(p)*. And in case (2) we could say: There really is a motion involved; the system of axes has been rotated, reflected, or otherwise displaced—so that the *X*-axis is now where the *Y*-axis used to be, for example. Hence, the two points of view are equivalent.

d. Metric Geometries

In Section 2c we concentrated on order relations and noted only that a notion of distance must be introduced if we wish to pass from affine to Euclidean geometry. Of course, the non-Euclidean geometries discussed in Section 2b also utilize the notion of distance. They cannot be obtained by adding to affine geometry, however, for in affine geometry one has the axiom that through a point outside a line *l* there is exactly one line *l'* parallel to *l*.[21] This is characteristic of Euclidean geometry. But when we discussed the introduction of coordinates, we did not assume anything about parallelism. We turn now to a different development in geometry in the nineteenth century, one that concerns the geometries in which the concept of distance is utilized (*metric geometries*).

In 1854, a brilliant young mathematician presented his dissertation (for his *Habilitation*) at the University of Göttingen. His name was Bernhard Riemann, and the now famous dissertation was called "On the Hypotheses Which Lie at the Foundations of Geometry."[22] In this work, Riemann presented the general concept of a manifold: the spectrum of color hues is a one-dimensional manifold, and space, as ordinarily conceived, is a three-dimensional manifold. The term "manifold" is not much in use any more; today we speak of spaces instead of manifolds. Riemann defined an *n*-dimensional space to be one in which each position can be characterized by a set of *n* coordinates. Thus, he envisaged spaces of more than three dimensions.

Given such a space, Riemann asked how the parts may be compared as to magnitude. Here he distinguished two main cases: the discrete and the continuous. In a discrete space, the elements in two regions may be counted and the two numbers compared in the usual way. In the discrete case, we may say that the space has an *intrinsic* metric, because counting provides us with a unique natural means of comparing magnitudes. But in the case of a continuous manifold, there is no such natural way of comparing the magnitudes of disjoint parts. The metric for a continuous space must be *extrinsic,* that is, introduced "from outside."[23] This subject, of the metrics that may be introduced into a continuous space, was Riemann's major topic of concern.

We introduce a metric by defining the distance between two points in terms of their coordinates. Using $d(p,q)$ to stand for the distance between the points p and q, the following conditions must be satisfied:

(a) $d(p,p) = 0$
(b) If $d(p,q) = 0$, then $p = q$ (sometimes omitted)
(c) $d(p,q) = d(q,p)$
(d) $d(p,q) + d(q,r) \geq d(p,r)$

These conditions are satisfied by the Euclidean distance function:

$d(p,q) = \sqrt{(x' - x)^2 + (y' - y)^2}$ where p and q have coordinates (x,y) and (x',y')

but there are many other distance functions, all of which satisfy the conditions above. And this provides a new approach to the non-Euclidean geometries.

Here I wish to point out first that the concept of distance provides a powerful tool in the construction of geometries, for the metric geometries can be developed with only *point* and *distance* as basic notions. For example, in Euclidean geometry, we can define "$p,q,$ and r lie on the same line" as $d(p,q) + d(q,r) = d(p,r)$, and "line l' is perpendicular to line l''" using Pythagoras' theorem. Then, we can choose three mutually perpendicular lines as axes, with their intersection as origin, and assign coordinates using distances from this origin.

So we can define a *metric space* simply as a collection of points with as metric a distance function on that collection. The appropriate choice of collection and distance function leads, then, to Euclidean geometry, or hyperbolic geometry, or spherical geometry, or elliptic geometry.[24] Each of these geometries can be axiomatized by spelling out the exact appropriate conditions on the concept of distance.

As Riemann pointed out, however, it is also possible to introduce metrics that lead to still different geometries. But as we mentioned in Section 2b, Lie proved that in these further geometries the principle of free mobility does not hold. We are now in a better position to understand this principle.

Helmholtz concerned himself with the question of exactly what principles are common to Euclidean and to non-Euclidean metric geometries. He arrived at four axioms, which we shall here summarize.[25]

(I)   The space of *n* dimensions is an *n*-dimensional extended manifold, in the sense of Riemann.

(II) There exist movable rigid bodies: between the coordinates of any two points in a rigid body there must be an equation that expresses a constant relation between the two points and that is the same for congruent pairs of points.

(III) Rigid bodies have complete free mobility: any single point can pass freely from any position to any other position, and a body can move with a point subject to the constancy of relations noted in the previous axiom.

(IV) Rotation in one direction brings a rigid body back into its original position. (Monodromy)

The language of these axioms is imprecise, even for an informal exposition, and it must be admitted that Helmholtz's work had a number of weak points.

To what, exactly, does this notion of free mobility amount? Recall that the plane of spherical geometry is geometrically like the surface of a Euclidean sphere. Suppose that a triangle of a certain size and shape is constructed at the equator. Then we can construct a similar and equal (i.e., congruent) triangle at its north pole or anywhere else on it. For which great circle is the equator is purely a matter of convention. Now Riemann's new geometries are such that their planes are geometrically just like very differently curved surfaces—for example, the surface of an egg. Such a surface is not everywhere the same: it is not a matter of convention which part of the egg is the sharper pole and which the flatter pole. And on such sur-

faces we may not be able to construct one triangle at some
point and a triangle congruent to the first at any other point.
If we construct a triangle at the flatter pole of an egg, and then
a triangle with equally long sides at the sharper pole, their
angles will not be equal. To put it another way: you cannot
slide the first triangle into a position at the sharper pole without wrinkling it.

The conclusions drawn by Helmholtz were made precise
and rigorously proved by Lie, who replaced the intuitive
terminology of rigid bodies by that of continuous transformations which preserve congruence.[26] He then showed that his
precise counterparts to Helmholtz's axioms allow for the four
"ordinary" metric geometries and exclude all others.

3. The Physical Basis
of Spatial Relations

When non-Euclidean geometries had been developed, the
obvious question was: Which geometry is the correct one?
Certainly, at first sight, this is a straightforward question. In
Euclidean geometry, the sum of the interior angles of a triangle
is 180°, in hyperbolic geometry it is less than 180°, and in
spherical geometry it is more than 180°. So Lobatchevsky
suggested that measurements should be made to determine
which alternatives actually obtain. Since the discrepancy increases with area, it is important to choose a "large enough"
triangle.

For this reason it was proposed that the evidence, if obtain-
able at all, should come from stellar parallax measurements.
The idea here is to sight a star from two different positions on
earth, A and B: the angles of the lines of sight at A and B are
the base angles of a large triangle; the distance between A and
B is the length of the base of the triangle. This information
may be used to compute the sum of the interior angles; for example if the angles at A and B equaled 180°, spherical geometry would be right.

It is important to see what is being assumed about the physical relations that correspond to the geometric concepts. First,
a star is sighted, that is, a light ray from that star falls on the

telescope. This ray provides the line of sight, and it is assumed that this line is straight (except for refraction by the atmosphere, perhaps, for which we may correct). So we have first the principle

(1) The path of a light ray *in vacuo* is a straight line.

Second, we must measure distances (the distance between *A* and *B*; also, distance measurements may be used to find the angle between the line of sight and the line $\overline{AB}$). There we use a calibrated rigid body, which we move from place to place to serve as standard. In doing so, we are going by the principle that this body remains the same size (except for distortions by temperature and such, for which we may correct):

(2) A rigid body free of distorting influences remains the same size when transported.

What is the status of principles (1) and (2)?

This question was discussed at length by Poincaré. We have already considered the more general philosophical points to be made on this subject in connection with clocks, in Chapter III. In the present context, Poincaré argues that which geometry is the correct one is not a matter of experiment at all. If parallax measurements were not to show an interior-angle sum of 180°, two courses would be open to us: "we might either renounce Euclidean geometry, or else modify the laws of optics and suppose that light does not travel rigorously in a straight line."[27]

Thus, Poincaré says that principles (1) and (2) are purely conventions. Measurement cannot disclose that they are correct, for they provide the standard of measurement. Whether we wish to accept them is a matter of decision, and the importance of simplicity and technical convenience in science, rather than truth, is relevant to this decision.

This is not to say that there are no questions of fact involved in the decision; as we pointed out before, even conventions may have empirical presuppositions. For example, it is here presupposed that the path of a light ray from *A* to *B* will be the shortest path as measured by a ruler. Also, if a ruler shows rigid stick X to be 1-meter long, and rigid stick Y to be 1-meter long, then it should be possible to bring X and Y in exact co-incidence.

Helmholtz also argued very graphically that whether "our" space is Euclidean is not a factual question.[28] He asked his audience to think of the image of the world in a convex mirror. "The image of a man measuring with a rule a straight line from the mirror would contract more and more the farther he went, but with his shrunken rule the man in the image would count out exactly the same number of centimetres as the real man."[29] So if it were theoretically useful, we could consistently look upon the space in which we live as being the space behind the convex mirror, but we would have to ascribe to our bodies the kind of distortions that we now see in such a mirror—just as Poincaré pointed out that we might have to ascribe curved trajectories to light rays if we wish to retain Euclidean geometry.

What this amounts to, of course, is that we may choose alternative metrics for space. Given some such metric, the size and shape of what we now call solid bodies may vary with position. But our present metric is such (by principle [2]) that the size of such a body varies only if it is subject to a distorting force. So if we choose an alternative metric, are we not postulating the existence of new forces, which cause the geometric distortions of the (formerly called "solid") bodies?

Of course, the answer is No: when we choose a metric, we only choose a way to describe the world; we do not postulate the existence of forces. In classical physics, all distortions of an iron rod are correlated with forces; if we choose an alternative metric, this physics must be redeveloped in such a way that this is no longer the case. For a long time, this was not seen very clearly; Reichenbach introduced the notion of universal forces to accompany, in appropriate manner, the choice of any metric,[30] and in his preface to Reichenbach's book Rudolf Carnap praises this idea highly. That its introduction is in fact based on a mistaken question ("What causes these distortions?") is shown in detail by Grünbaum.[31] But the issue is similar to the one between Russell and Poincaré with respect to alternative metrics for time (see Chapter III, Section 2c), so we shall leave it here.

Today we generally distinguish between a *mathematical geometry* and a *physical geometry*. A mathematical geometry is a purely abstract, deductive system, with nothing to say about physical relations. It can be turned into a physical geometry by adding such principles as (1) and (2); so a physical geometry is a rudimentary physical theory.

Principles such as (1) and (2) were called *coordinative definitions* by Reichenbach.[32] This term is somewhat misleading, because a definition is supposed to have the form ". . . if and only if . . ." But (1) has the form

(1′) If $\overline{ABC}$ is the path of a light ray, then it is a straight line.

A definition would have to go further than 1′, to say something like

(1″) The path $\overline{ABC}$ is a straight line if and only if it is the path of a light ray.

But this would imply that there are no straight lines in the dark. Also, it would imply that there are no straight lines that pass through opaque objects. So we need something like

(1‴) The path $\overline{ABC}$ is a straight line if and only if it could be the path of a light ray.

This is not a very pleasing development, since this version makes use of the counterfactual sense of "could"; as we have already mentioned, there are many philosophical puzzles about this. But this is not the only place where we appear to need the counterfactual conditional: the same problem arises with respect to (2). For an object is 1-meter long not only if it is brought into exact coincidence with the meter standard kept in Paris, but if this could be done.

Tentatively, we may conclude the following: A mathematical geometry describes what we have previously called a logical space. The coordinative definitions place or map physical objects and relationships in this space. But they cannot do this with complete definiteness unless we allow them to rely on counterfactual assertions. This is a problem that we shall examine in more detail, and in a more contemporary setting, in Chapter VI.

4. The Dimensionality of Space

Space has three dimensions; but what does this mean? And why is it so? The first question had no adequate answer until this century; the second has a long and interesting history, and is still the subject of some puzzlement. Nor were the two questions always clearly distinguished. Here we shall follow two approaches to the subject of dimensionality: we shall consider the purely geometric relationships that define dimensionality, and then we shall inquire into the physical basis for these relationships.

a. The Concept of Dimensionality

The discussion of dimensionality begins in antiquity, but we may conveniently begin with Leibniz.[33] In the *Theodicy*, Leibniz says that in geometry we can prove that there are only three straight lines perpendicular to one another that can intersect at one and the same point and that this shows that space has necessarily exactly three dimensions.[34] What is of interest to us here is the implied definition: A space is n-dimensional if we can draw n lines perpendicular to each other at a given point. This definition works only for metric geometry, of course, since it uses the notion of the magnitude of an angle.

As we noted above, Riemann defined an n-dimensional space as one in which each position can be uniquely characterized by just n coordinates. If we consider only Cartesian coordinates, then this definition is the same as Leibniz's definition. But of course Riemann assumed the coordinates to have been introduced before the metric, so his definition is more general.

But Riemann's definition is not adequate as it stands. For we now know that there are just as many points on a line as there are on a plane. So to each point on the plane we can assign a unique point on the line. The single real-number coordinate of the second point can now be assigned to the first point, and thus, we have coordinatized the plane by means of numbers rather than pairs of numbers.

The objection to this procedure is obvious: we expect more of coordinates than that they provide each point with a unique label. If we draw any continuous curve in the plane, the coordinates of its points should also form a continuum. Will the nonstandard coordinates of the preceding paragraph have this property? That the answer is No was proved in 1911 by the Dutch mathematician L. E. J. Brouwer.[35] He proved that there is no continuous one-to-one transformation between Euclidean spaces of different dimensionality. So if we insist that an assignment of coordinates reflect the topological properties of the space, then Riemann's definition may still serve.

But if dimension is a topological invariant, then the detour via coordinates is superfluous and dimensionality should be defined in topological terms. This was first done by Poincaré. By a *cut* Poincaré means a collection of points removed from a continuous region. It may happen that a cut divides the continuum into disjoint continuous regions. If a continuum *C* can be divided by a cut that does not itself form a continuum, then *C* is *one-dimensional*. If a continuum is not one-dimensional, but can be divided by one-dimensional cuts, then it is *two-dimensional*—and so on. For example, a line can be divided by the removal of a point, a closed curve by the removal of several points, a plane by the removal of a line, and so on.[36]

This definition was not adequate to all cases and Brouwer replaced it by a new definition in 1913. Essentially, he used the notion of a *boundary* that separates two continuous regions: a boundary is such that any continuous path from one region to the other must pass through it. This is, of course, very much like Poincaré's cut. The definition was further improved by Karl Menger and Paul Urysohn in 1922.[37]

b. The Physical Basis of Dimensionality

What are the physical relationships that correspond to the geometric feature of dimensionality? There have been two approaches to this question, roughly paralleling the two stages in the development of the geometric concept; the first approach concentrates on numerical magnitudes, and the second on more basic features of the physical world.

The first approach was initiated by Kant in his early essay "Thoughts on the True Estimation of Living Forces" (1747). After pointing out that Leibniz's remarks in the *Theodicy* cannot, without circularity, be taken to show that space could not have other than three dimensions, Kant speculates on the physical basis of dimensionality.[38] His speculation has an extremely contemporary ring to it; no similar ideas were developed until Riemann's work a century later. Kant's theory is that the structure of space has as its physical basis the forces that bodies exert on each other. He maintains that the three-dimensionality of space is due to the fact that these forces vary inversely with the square of the distances between bodies. Here he is clearly thinking of Newton's famous law of gravitation, which asserts this of gravitational attraction. Kant adds that this law is not a necessary one—God could have chosen another—and "from a different law an extension with other properties and dimensions would have arisen."

But what is the connection here? This was answered in detail by Friedrich Ueberweg in his *System der Logik* (1882).[39] Let us assume that every point at a given distance r from the body receives a proportional part of the total force it exerts on all the points at that distance. In a plane the locus of equidistant points is the circumference of a circle, with its magnitude proportional to r. In a three-dimensional space, this locus is the surface of a sphere, its magnitude proportional to r^2. Thus, if the total amount of force exerted does not change with the distance, the force exerted on any given point will vary inversely with the distance in a two-dimensional space, with the square of the distance in a three-dimensional space, and so on.

A similar, but less specific, answer utilizes the following theorem of mechanics: A circular or nearly circular orbit about a force center is stable when the force is inversely proportional to the mth power of the distance if and only if m is less than three.[40] So if space had four dimensions, gravitational attraction would presumably be inversely proportional to the cube of the distance, but no planets would orbit the sun.

A still more sophisticated, and less specific, answer utilizes a theorem about the possibility of wave propagation such as that of light. The theorem implies that the transmission of waves of this sort, in the manner postulated by the theory, is possible only if space has an odd number of dimensions.[41]

The objection to this approach is that dimensionality is not a metric but a topological feature of space. Hence, the features of the physical world pointed out above are simply not basic enough to shed much light on the dimensionality of space. As Russell pointed out, a small inaccuracy might exist in the accepted law of gravitation and remain undetected, but not so in the principle that space is three-dimensional.[42] There is however, one variant of this approach that relies on the metric concept of congruence, but is not such that Russell's remark applies.

This variant was also due to Kant, though he does not seem to have thought of it in this way. In his early essay "On the First Ground of the Distinction of Regions in Space" (1768), he points out that if two figures drawn on a plane are equal and similar, they can be superimposed (are congruent); but this is not so for solids.[43] For example, if we draw a left hand and a right hand on paper, and cut out the right hand, we can turn it upside down and superimpose it exactly on the left hand. But there is no way of putting a right-hand glove on an actual left hand. Kant did not see this, at the time, as having to do with dimensions. The point is, of course, that the paper right hand cannot be superimposed on the left hand by means of motions *in the plane*. What is needed is a rotation through the third dimension. In general, n-dimensional mirror images can be superimposed only by means of a rotation in $(n + 1)$-dimensional space.[44]

Although this argument relies on the metric notion of congruence, the point it makes is much more fundamental than that of the others, because some of its main features are topological. We can divide the Euclidean transformations into those that move figures through a continuous path and those that do not. Thus, a rotation can be regarded as the result of a series of successive transformations, each of which moves the figure only infinitesimally. But a reflection—the kind of transformation that produces mirror images—cannot be thought of in this way. A reflection is defined by the fact that it leaves a certain plane unaffected and transposes all figures from one side of that plane to the other. If we were to try to trace a continuous path that a figure follows to become its own mirror image on the other side of the plane, the path would have to be through that plane. (The plane is a boundary between the two regions, in Brouwer's sense.) But that would mean that the transformation is affecting some of the points of that plane; and it cannot put those points back into their own place by means of a continuous rigid motion, without placing the figure back where it was also. This is just an intuitive, pictorial exposition, but it may help to see the topological distinction between a reflection and a rotation. The effect of a reflection can be achieved through a continuous motion if there is a way to get "around" or "over" the dividing plane, but that requires a fourth dimension.

The second approach to the physical basis of dimensionality, finally, means to rely only on topological features. It was apparently developed only by Reichenbach.[45] The basic idea is that all causal interaction satisfies the principle of *action by contact:* all causal effects move through a continuous path in space, with a finite velocity.* This means that a true "locked-room murder" is excluded as impossible. I can step over the boundary of a closed curve, but I cannot step over the boundary of a closed volume. Reichenbach sees this not as an empirical truth but as a basic feature of what we mean by "our" space or "real" space:

> *The principle of action by contact can be satisfied only for a single choice of the dimensionality of the parameter space; this particular parameter space in which it is satisfied is called the coordinate space or "real space."*[46]

That the principle of action by contact cannot be satisfied for more than one choice of the dimensionality follows from the fact that there is no continuous one-to-one transformation between spaces of different dimensionality, according to Reichenbach.

---

* To define this we need clocks (a metric for time) and the requirement that in any spatial metric, there is a nonzero distance between distinct points: no specific spatial metric is presupposed.

In my opinion, Reichenbach's is the correct approach, since it is concerned only with topological features. But there are several problems. The first is that his answer is not really complete unless he gives a (nonspatial) description of the relationships that may constitute a causal process. There is some indication, however, that he is willing to replace the general, and at least vague, notion of causal process with that of light signal and/or genidentity connection. Second, his criterion does not necessarily rule out all but one dimensionality for space, unless either every continuous path is actually the locus of some causal process or we allow him also to rely on possible causal processes. For it is possible for a continuous transformation to change dimensionality, provided it is not a one-to-one transformation.

There is also another problem, which no one has tried to answer as far as I know. Our space is three-dimensional; therefore, it certainly has room for two-dimensional beings. So why aren't there any? Or couldn't we tell, even if there were? And about the possibility of a fourth dimension I think we feel puzzled in much the same way as about time travel. We can imagine phenomena that would be explained, prima facie, by the hypothesis that there is time travel, or travel through a fourth dimension. But I am inclined to think that we would prefer almost any hypothesis to either of these, because I cannot see how we could possibly plot the correct trajectory of some object outside our own space-time (as opposed to postulating that it must have some such trajectory). Poincaré, however, announced with great confidence that physicists would always prefer Euclidean geometry to any other, so I am not inclined to make this a prediction.

Chapter V

The Impact
of the
Theory of
Relativity

In the development of the theory of time and space before 1900, the relational theory (though philosophically the more attractive) was left with a major unsolved problem. This is the problem of providing an explicit theory of temporal and spatial order; that is, of exhibiting explicitly the physical relationships among events that supposedly constitute their spatiotemporal relations. Leibniz constructed such a theory, but it was based on the rationalist theory of causality; after Hume, the presumption that time order can be defined in terms of causation could not seem plausible. Kant addressed himself to this problem in the *Analogies,* but the answer there is too general to be considered more than programmatic. When Lechalas attempted to provide cash value for this approach, he failed—and not because of simple or superficial problems.

1. The Revolution in the Theory of Time and Space

In setting a problem, as in asking a question, we may be subject to certain presuppositions, and these presuppositions may not be satisfied. The possibility of a topologically closed time must convince us that the search for a physical correlate for the *before-after* relation (as ordinarily conceived) may have such a mistaken presupposition. Indeed, this applies also to the case of temporal betweenness, as we have seen. And even if time is open, so that we must find a physical basis of temporal betweenness, there may be no physical anisotrophy of the kind needed to give an entirely nonconventional definition of *before*. But by 1900, these presuppositions had been made explicit, and the formulation of the problem of time (and space) order can take them into account.

The great importance of Albert Einstein's development of the theory of relativity, for our subject, lies in two facts: (1) it exhibits a similar factual presupposition in the problem of finding a physical correlate for simultaneity, and (2) it exhibits such an intimate interdependence of temporal and spatial relations that time and space can no longer be treated as essentially independent subjects. Philosophers were not long in appreciating the revolutionary nature of this development, and the consequent construction of the causal theory of time and space-time must be considered one of the major contributions of twentieth-century philosophy of science.

It is clear then that anyone who wishes to grasp the twentieth-century development of the philosophy of time and space must acquaint himself with the elements of the special theory of relativity. (The general theory of relativity is also of importance for this subject, but we shall not go beyond the special theory.) Since this theory is concerned with the relations between different frames of reference, and our own experience as well as classical physics leads us quite naturally to conceive of the world from the perspective of a single frame of reference, acquainting ourselves with the theory necessitates the rethinking of many basic concepts.

Fortunately, the fifty years devoted to philosophical and logical investigation of the special theory of relativity have brought us to the point where its elements can be presented quite simply. This discussion will not teach any relativistic kinematics or dynamics, and many standard questions are ignored. There are, after all, many popular presentations of the subject. Only what is absolutely essential to the theory of time and space will be presented here.

2. The Classical Point of View and the Lorentz Hypotheses

a. The Michelson-Morley Experiment and Length Contraction

Classical physics accounted for the phenomena of sound as being occasioned by waves propagated in air. This account is, of course, subject to experimental verification: wavelike propagation follows different laws from, say, propagation by traveling particles. When Christiaan Huygens' theory that the propagation of light is also wavelike had found acceptance, physicists postulated an all-pervasive, space-filling medium as the carrier of light waves. This medium was called the ether.

Given the Newtonian theory of absolute space, it makes sense to ask: Is this ether at rest or in motion? The propagation of a wave in a river is different from that in a pond, due to the current; it is not difficult to appreciate that experimental evidence can be relevant to this question. It was found that the hypothesis that the ether is in absolute motion would contradict the experimental results. Hence, it was concluded that the ether is at rest with respect to absolute space. (This is a good example of how experimental findings are used to provide answers to theoretical questions. Only the presupposition of our question—that everything is either in absolute motion or at absolute rest—justifies the conclusion "at rest" from the denial of "in motion.")

So the ether is at rest, and light is propagated in it; and the obvious (and simplest) hypothesis is that its speed relative to the ether has some uniform value c (independent of how the light was produced). This is then also its absolute velocity. The earth on the other hand travels in an elliptical orbit around the sun; hence, its absolute velocity must be different at different times. This means that the relative velocity of light with respect to the earth must also be different at different times. Therefore, the absolute motion of the earth must be detectable, simply by detecting this variation in the relative velocity of light with respect to the earth. An experiment was devised for this purpose by James Clerk Maxwell and first carried out with sufficient precision by Michelson and Morley in 1887.[1]

Before discussing this experiment and its surprising outcome, it is well to inquire whether it could possibly show conclusively that the earth is in absolute motion. The reasoning in the preceding paragraph is predicated, after all, on the prior conclusion that the ether is at rest with respect to absolute space. It must be noted that this very conclusion concerning the ether provides an out for the relational theory of space. The Newtonian has deduced that the ether has absolute velocity zero; hence, "absolute velocity v" is equivalent to "relative velocity v with respect to the ether." Thus, the Newtonian analysis of the velocity variable v as ranging over the values of relative velocity with respect to absolute space could now be paralleled by an analysis in terms of velocity relative to the ether. Given an all-pervasive stationary ether, it would seem that the hypothesis of absolute space may become superfluous. Thus, if the outcome of the experiment were to agree with the Newtonian's expectations, its lesson would nevertheless be ambiguous.

The basic structure of the Michelson-Morley experiment is quite simple. A ray of light falls on a semireflecting mirror A, set at such an angle that half the ray is reflected toward mirror B and half is allowed to pass on to mirror C. Mirrors B and C reflect those half rays. AB and AC are equal and perpendicular to each other, so it follows that if the apparatus is at rest in the ether, the two half rays return to A coincidently.

Suppose, however, that the apparatus is moving to the right, with velocity v relative to the ether and AB perpendicular to the direction of motion. In the time it takes the light to go from A to B, the apparatus will have shifted a bit. And it will shift the same amount during the return of the light from B to A. Let A now indicate the position of the mirror at the begin-

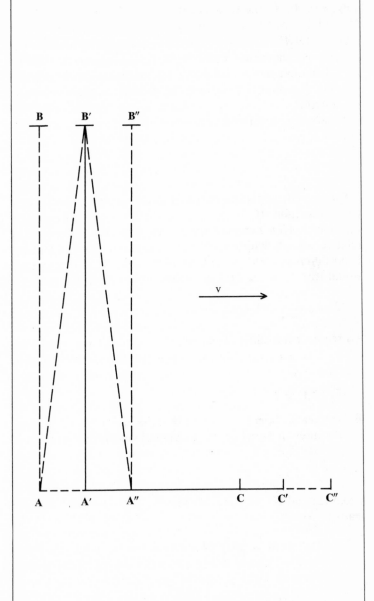

Figure 2

ning, and A', A'' the subsequent positions; similarly for B, B', B'' and C, C', C'' (see Figure 2). The light now makes the journey $AB'A''$ rather than ABA, a distance $2L'$ rather than $2L$. Since L' is greater than L, this trip should take longer. A careful calculation shows that this difference has as result that the two half rays should *not* return coincidently at the semireflecting mirror.

Case 1. The apparatus is at rest relative to the ether. Then both half rays take for their round trip the amount of time

(1) $\Delta t = \dfrac{2L}{c}$

Case 2. The apparatus moves through the ether at velocity v in the direction AC.

a. Since AB is perpendicular to the direction of motion, the relative velocity with respect to the apparatus of *that* half ray is no different. But as we have seen, it has to make a longer round trip $AB'A'' = 2L'$. So its round-trip time is

(2) $\Delta_1 = \dfrac{2L'}{c}$

To see how this differs from Δt, we must evaluate L' in terms of L. Let $AA' = A'A'' = k$. Then by Pythagoras' theorem, we have

(3) $(L')^2 = L^2 + k^2$

But of course, $2k$ is the distance that the apparatus moves during the interval Δ_1, while it is moving at velocity v. Hence,

(4) $k = \dfrac{v\Delta_1}{2}$

From (2) and (4) we conclude that $k = v(L'/c)$. Therefore, (3) leads us to

(5) $(L')^2 = L^2 + \left(\dfrac{L'}{c}\right)^2 v^2$

(6) $L' = \dfrac{L}{\sqrt{1 - (v^2/c^2)}}$

Together (2) and (6) yield

(7) $\Delta_1 = \dfrac{2L}{c\sqrt{1 - (v^2/c^2)}} = \Delta t \dfrac{1}{\sqrt{1 - (v^2/c^2)}}$

which is somewhat greater than Δt.

b. The other half ray must travel the same distance as before; its relative velocity with respect to the apparatus is affected by the latter's motion, however. On the trip outward, the relative velocity is diminished to $c - v$; on the return trip it is increased to $c + v$. Thus, the round-trip time is

(8) $\Delta_2 = \dfrac{L}{c - v} + \dfrac{L}{c - v}$

$= \dfrac{2Lc}{c^2 - v^2}$

To evaluate this in terms of Δt, we see from (1) that we must isolate a factor $2L/c$. This is done as follows:

(9) $\Delta_2 = \dfrac{2Lc}{c^2 - v^2}$

$= \dfrac{2L}{c(1 - (v^2/c^2))}$

(10) $\Delta_2 = \Delta t \left(\dfrac{1}{1 - (v^2/c^2)}\right)$

Note that this is greater than Δt, but also greater than Δ_1: from (7) and (10) we get

(11) $\Delta_2 = \Delta_1 \dfrac{1}{\sqrt{1 - (v^2/c^2)}}$

Thus, Δt is less than Δ_1 and Δ_1 less than Δ_2, in each case through multiplication with the factor $1/\sqrt{1 - (v^2/c^2)}$.

What we have just calculated is the classically expected outcome of the Michelson-Morley experiment: the two half rays do not return coincidently to the point of origin. But in fact, the experiment had a different outcome: the half rays did return coincidently. The experiment was repeated, and similar experiments were devised to check it; in each case, the result was negative. No variation in the relative velocity of earth and light could be detected. The earth's supposed velocity relative to the ether appeared to be inconsistent with the experimental results.

There were, of course, many theoretical attempts to save the ether hypothesis.[2] Only one of these is now important: the attempt of G. F. Fitzgerald and Hendrik Lorentz. Fitzgerald pointed out that the null result of the Michelson-Morley experiment would follow from the hypothesis that the arm AC, lying along the direction of motion, contracts by a factor of $\sqrt{1 - (v^2/c^2)}$. Then its length is not L but $L\sqrt{1 - (v^2/c^2)}$ and the evaluation of Δ_2 yields not (9) but

$$(12) \quad \Delta_2 = \frac{2(L\sqrt{1 - (v^2/c^2)}\,)c}{c^2 - v^2}$$

$$= \frac{2L}{c}\left(\frac{1}{\sqrt{1 - (v^2/c^2)}}\right) = \Delta_1$$

It would be ad hoc simply to accept this hypothesis in order to account for the outcome of the Michelson-Morley experiment. But Lorentz developed a theory of atomic structure that had this length-contraction hypothesis as a deductive consequence.[3] This had to be considered an important point in favor of Lorentz's theory of the atom.

b. The Fizeau Experiment and Time Dilation

It is clear that the contraction hypothesis, and hence Lorentz's theory, entails that the results of length measurement are systematically mistaken. In any measurement of spatial magnitudes, the measuring rod contracts along the direction of its absolute motion, by a factor dependent on its absolute velocity —and this absolute velocity apparently cannot be determined, just because of this contraction.

We may well ask what happens to time measurement. It will be recalled that Poincaré's light clock resembles one arm of the Michelson-Morley apparatus (see Chapter III, Section 2b). The complete apparatus consists of two Poincaré light clocks, which are coincident but differently oriented. The presupposition of a definition of a unit of duration in terms of this light clock was that coincident light clocks of the same construction should agree. And this is exactly the actual (though unexpected) null outcome of the experiment. We might sum up the matter as follows: classical theory says that the use of the light clock for duration measurements is based on a mistaken presupposition; Lorentz's theory, because it entails the contraction hypothesis, says that on the contrary this presupposition is satisfied. Thus, we must also be prepared for this hypothesis about spatial magnitudes to have significant consequences for the theory of time measurement.

A typical mechanical clock is a mechanism known as a harmonic oscillator. Lorentz showed that it followed from his theory that such a clock slows down when in absolute motion, by a factor depending on its absolute velocity.[4] The hypothesis that this is so, is known as the hypothesis of *time dilation*. To see exactly how much a moving clock must slow down, we shall consider an experiment that has the effect of comparing a light clock with a standard (mechanical) clock. If there is a discrepancy between the two, this discrepancy might be used to confirm the hypothesis of the earth's motion through the ether—in exactly the way that a discrepancy between two differently oriented light clocks was supposed to do in the Michelson-Morley experiment. The experiment to which we refer was designed by Armande Fizeau; this could not be carried out with sufficient precision until fairly recently, but Lorentz correctly predicted its outcome.[5]

Light is passed through a toothed wheel A across a distance L to a mirror B, which reflects the rays back to A. The speed of the toothed wheel is adjusted so that the returning light comes through a succeeding tooth. The speed of the wheel is measured by means of a standard clock; hence, we know the magnitude Δt of the time interval for one tooth to replace another at the position in question. As long as the apparatus is at rest in the ether we have, as before,

(13) $\Delta t = \dfrac{2L}{c}$

Since an ordinary clock has allowed us to measure Δt, and we presumably know L, this result can be used to calculate c. Now suppose the apparatus has an absolute velocity in the direction AB. Then, on the classical theory the round-trip time changes from Δt to

$$(14) \quad \Delta = \frac{L}{c + v} + \frac{L}{c - v} = \frac{2L}{c} \left(\frac{1}{1 - (v^2/c^2)} \right)$$

and on Lorentz's theory, which incorporates the contraction hypothesis, it changes to

$$(15) \quad \Delta' = \frac{L\sqrt{1 - (v^2/c^2)}}{c + v} + \frac{L\sqrt{1 - (v^2/c^2)}}{c - v}$$

$$= \frac{2L}{c} \left(\frac{1}{\sqrt{1 - (v^2/c^2)}} \right)$$

In either case, the round-trip time is a function of the absolute velocity *v*. Hence, if our standard mechanical clocks (used to measure the speed of the toothed wheel) give the correct result, *and* the apparatus is rigidly affixed to the earth, *and* the earth's relative velocity with respect to the ether is different at different times of the year, this variation in the round-trip time will be detectable. But Lorentz correctly predicted that this variation (and hence, the earth's motion through the ether) could not be detected. According to Lorentz, the actual round-trip time is, of course, Δ', as given by (15), but the clock's measurement will show the result Δt. From (13) and (15) we deduce

$$(16) \quad \Delta t = \Delta' \left(\sqrt{1 - (v^2/c^2)} \right)$$

so that the clock must have slowed down by a factor of $\sqrt{1 - (v^2/c^2)}$.

c. The Lorentz Transformations

The hypotheses of length contraction and time dilation together entail that measurements by different observers (in uniform motion relative to each other, and not subject to forces of the kind that Newton attributed to absolute acceleration) will give systematically different results. We now face the following theoretical question: Given two observers *A* and *B* such that *B*'s velocity relative to *A* is *v*, what is the relation between their respective measurement results? The solution to this problem is given by the Lorentz transformations.

We suppose that the observers *A* and *B* use their measuring rods and clocks to assign a date (time coordinate) and also three space coordinates to each event, in the usual manner.

Let us use t, x, y, z for the coordinates assigned to an event by A, and t', x', y', z' for those assigned by B. For simplicity suppose that they choose the same *origin* for their coordinate system: the event with the coordinates $t = x = y = z = 0$ also has the coordinates $t' = x' = y' = z' = 0$. Again, for simplicity suppose that B moves along A's X-axis; that is, the y and z coordinates are always the same as the y' and z' coordinates:

(17) $y' = y$
$\quad\ z' = z$

Then the Lorentz transformation in addition expresses t' and x' in terms of t and x:

(18) $t' = \dfrac{t - xv/c^2}{\sqrt{1 - (v^2/c^2)}}$

$\quad\ x' = \dfrac{x - vt}{\sqrt{1 - (v^2/c^2)}}$

Note that v here is the relative velocity of B to A, but c is the absolute velocity of light. If we decide to choose our units such that $c = 1$, the Lorentz transformations take a very simple form:

(19) $t' = \dfrac{t - xv}{\sqrt{1 - v^2}}$

$\quad\ x' = \dfrac{x - vt}{\sqrt{1 - v^2}}$

The results of the measurements of distance and duration clearly vary from observer to observer, if the observers are in relative motion. A second, equally important question is: Is there any quantity that is *not* thus relative to the frame of reference?

This is the question for a quantity that (unlike duration and distance) is invariant under the Lorentz transformations. There is such a quantity, namely, the *space-time interval*. Let events X and Y be separated by a time interval Δt and by a space interval Δd (as measured, in each case, in the frame of reference of a single observer A). Then, the space-time interval $s(X, Y)$ separating X and Y has the magnitude

$\sqrt{(\Delta t)^2 - (\Delta d)^2}$. (This definition presupposes, of course, that this magnitude is independent of the choice of a frame of reference; otherwise, we would have to say that this space-time interval has this magnitude *in A's frame of reference.*)

Using the Fizeau experiment, we can calculate the speed of light relative to the apparatus; this turns out to be the same value c regardless of its state of motion. In other words, the speed of light is the same in each frame of reference. This fact is related to the invariance of the space-time interval as follows. Suppose a light signal leaves at $t = 0$ the origin of a frame S that is at absolute rest, and at t is found at (x,y,z). Let c be its absolute speed. Then it has traveled a distance ct. But also, it has traveled the distance from $(0,0,0)$ to (x,y,z): a distance equal to $\sqrt{x^2 + y^2 + z^2}$. So we have

(20) $ct = \sqrt{x^2 + y^2 + z^2}$

Making no assumption about the relative speed of light with respect to any other frame of reference, we can still choose the absolute speed c to equal 1 in our system of units in this frame. Hence, (20) yields

(21) $t = \sqrt{x^2 + y^2 + z^2}$

or

(22) $t^2 = x^2 + y^2 + z^2$

But then the space-time interval between the events X at $t = 0$ and position $(0,0,0)$ and the event Y at t and position (x,y,z) is

(23) $\sqrt{t^2 - (x^2 + y^2 + z^2)} = \sqrt{t^2 - t^2} = 0$

Of course, we can duplicate this calculation for any two events in the path of the same light ray: the space-time interval between them, reckoned in the frame S, is always 0. Now the Lorentz transformations entail that the magnitude of the space-time interval will be the same in any other (unaccelerated) frame S'. So we *always* have the result

(24) $s(X,Y) = (\Delta t)^2 - (\Delta d)^2 = 0$

for such events X and Y; regardless of the frame of reference, $|\Delta t| = |\Delta d|$. Now $|\Delta t|$ is the duration of travel and $|\Delta d|$ is the distance covered; so the speed must be $|(\Delta d/\Delta t)| = 1$ in the other frames also.

In other words, the Lorentz transformations explain how (or why) the speed of light is found to be the same in all frames of reference. They explain this in the sense that they entail that result; for anyone who accepts the Lorentz theory, the sameness of the velocity of light in every frame of reference is exactly what is to be expected.

3. Einstein's Critique of Simultaneity

Lorentz's theory was, of course, explicitly based on the Newtonian interpretation of physics in terms of absolute space. At the same time, the physics envisioned by Lorentz is an extension of classical physics—an extension so designed that the unexpected experimental results of the late nineteenth century are accommodated. The relativistic physics developed by Einstein is not merely an extension of the classical theory; it is a different theory whose predictions of experimental outcomes differ at certain points from the classical expectations. But like Lorentz's theory, it has the virtue of predicting the null outcome of the Michelson-Morley and Fizeau experiments. Indeed, it entails that different *inertial frames* (the frames of reference of observers not subject to absolute acceleration, according to the classical view) are related to each other through the Lorentz transformations.

Most presentations of the special theory of relativity begin with a principle such as the following: The laws of physics are the same in all inertial frames (*restricted principle of relativity*). Since we are not interested in presenting relativistic physics, but only in explaining Einstein's concepts of time and space, we shall proceed differently. We shall reconstruct Einstein's exploration of the concept of simultaneity.[6] Doing so nevertheless leads, as we shall see, to a deduction of the Lorentz transformations.

Consider two observers, each of whom can tell the order of events in his own history. Suppose event X happens to the one and event Y to the other. Under what conditions are X and Y to be regarded as simultaneous?

A first answer might be in terms of perception: If the first observer perceives Y happening just when X happens to him, the two events are simultaneous. But this is quite incorrect, given that the velocity of light and sound is finite: If the observer sees Y, and Y is a distance d away, and the light has moved from Y to his eyes at an (average) speed c, then Y happened a time interval of magnitude d/c before he sees it.

The second answer simply corrects the oversight pointed out above: Let the observer measure the distance d and one-way speed of light c, and he can allow for the time it takes light to travel from the event to his eye. Now the important question is: How can the observer determine the one-way speed of light (or of sound, or whatever other signal is used; the problem will be similar)? Recall that in the Michelson-Morley experiments only the round-trip time of a reflected signal was directly measured. If we are also given the distance, we may calculate the average round-trip velocity. But what is the one-way velocity? Is it the same as the round-trip velocity? Certainly not, according to the classical theory. There we said that the speed of light in the Fizeau apparatus was $c + v$ one way and $c - v$ the other way, where v is the absolute velocity of the apparatus. And now we are properly caught: the Lorentz transformations guarantee that this absolute velocity cannot be determined. But of course, what the classical theory says is not of interest to us now, except to show that knowing the round-trip velocity does not guarantee knowing the one-way velocity. We must find some experimental method for determining this one-way velocity.

To measure a velocity we must be able to measure distance and duration. Suppose the signal travels from A to B. Then to find its velocity, we require the time at which it leaves A, the distance it covers, and the time at which it arrives at B. The time? Well, the time as reckoned by a given clock. Unfortunately light signals are so fast that we can't move a single clock from A to B between the emission and arrival of a single light signal. Then, let us use synchronized clocks: begin by placing two equivalent clocks at A, synchronizing them, and then move one of them to B. Recall that two clocks are equivalent if once they are synchronized they remain synchronized for as long as they are left coincident. We must now worry about what happens after these synchronized equivalent clocks are taken out of coincidence: does travel affect the second clock? According to Lorentz it does, of course; a clock slows down when it is in absolute motion. We cannot appeal to the notion of absolute motion here, but we can postulate the following verifiable effect of the time-dilation hypothesis: when the clocks are brought into coincidence again, they are no longer synchronized. This is the *clock postulate:* If two equivalent clocks are synchronized at *A* and are brought to *B* in such a way that either

(a) they arrive coincidently at *B*, but after traversing paths of different lengths

or

(b) they traverse paths of the same lengths, and their departures but not their arrivals at *B* coincide,

then they will be found *not* to be synchronized once they are together at *B*. Note that the Lorentz hypothesis of time dilation is formulated in terms of the notion of absolute velocity. The clock postulate is a consequence of that hypothesis, but it is also a purely empirical assertion, whose formulation needs no recourse to absolute notions.

Could transported equivalent clocks be used in some other way to define simultaneity?[7] That the answer could be affirmative is suggested by the fact that in Lorentz's theory, the exact discrepancy between moving clocks can be calculated from their velocities. But this overlooks the main problem that confronts us here: how to compare clocks that are apart spatially. Suppose that the clock postulate does not hold— that synchronized equivalent clocks are always found to be synchronized once they have been brought in coincidence again. Then what is the significance of asserting that they were also in agreement while they were apart? This assertion may seem intuitively to have an objective sense: they ran "equally," "at the same rate," even when they were apart spatially (they did not, for example, speed up on the outward journey and slow down on the return journey). But in fact we have no more objective basis for this than for the correlate assertion that on a round trip the velocity of a light signal on its journey equals its velocity on the return journey.

The upshot of this discussion is that we have no way of

determining one-way velocities—and hence simultaneity—unless we first have a way of synchronizing clocks that are apart spatially.

To see how in principle this might be done, we must once more have recourse to round-trip times. Let us suppose that a light signal is sent from *A* to *B*. Let *E*, *R*, and *F* be the following events:

(*E*) emission of the signal (at *A*),
(*R*) reflection of the signal (at *B*),
(*F*) arrival of the signal (at *A*).

If *x* is an event, let $t(X)$ be its date (time coordinate) in *A*'s frame of reference. *A* knows $t(E)$ and $t(F)$. What date should he assign to *R*? We don't know yet, but at least we must have $t(R)$ *between* $t(E)$ and $t(F)$. Now let us send a faster signal, adjusting its emission *E'* (after *E*) in such a way that its reflection *R'* at *B* is coincident with the event *R* (as an observer at *B* can determine). That the signal is of a faster kind means simply that

$$t(E') > t(E)$$

$$t(F') < t(F)$$

And we must also say that $t(R') = t(R)$, and a reflection is, of course, *between* an emission and a return: $t(E') < t(R') < t(F')$. Putting this information together, we see that

$$t(E') < t(R) < t(F')$$

which is a more precise determination of $t(R)$ than we obtained from the use of the first signal.

Thus, using ever faster signals, our determination of $t(R)$ will become ever more precise. So, by the use of ever faster signals, we can synchronize clocks at *A* and *B* to within any degree of accuracy. (That is, the mere requirement that causes be temporally before effects yields a unique simultaneity relation.)

This procedure presupposes, however, that there is no upper bound to signal velocities. And Einstein denies this presupposition: he asserts that no signal faster than light. This is the *limiting postulate:*

If a light signal S_1 and another signal S_2 are emitted coincidently at A and both reflected from another body B, and both return to A, then that return of S_1 is temporally *between* the joint emission of S_1 and S_2 *and* that return of S_2 at A.

The conclusion drawn by Einstein is as simple as it is revolutionary: There is no physical basis for the relation of simultaneity between events that are spatially separate.

But we are still left with the problem of assigning a time coordinate $t(R)$ to the event R, in A's frame of reference. If our first signal was already a light signal, then all the information we have is

(25) $t(E) < t(R) < t(F)$

If there is no physical basis for determining $t(R)$ more precisely than this, all we can do is introduce a convention. This convention must take the form of choosing a value ε and laying down the definition

(26) $t(R) = t(E) + \varepsilon[t(F) - t(E)]$

This value ε must satisfy

(27) $0 < \varepsilon < 1$

Otherwise, (26) is inconsistent with (25). Apart from that, the choice of ε is purely conventional: it may be a constant, or a function of $t(E)$, or a function of A, and so on (*conventionality of simultaneity*).

Einstein made the stipulation

(28) $\varepsilon = \dfrac{1}{2}$

This meant that $t(R)$ is exactly halfway between $t(E)$ and $t(F)$; in other words, in any frame of reference, the one-way speed of light is set (by this convention) equal to its average round-trip speed. This has the practical advantage of being a very simple convention. It also has the consequence that one and the same pair of events may be simultaneous in one frame of reference (in the sense of receiving the same time coordinate) and not in some other frame of reference (*relativity of simultaneity*).[8]

To illustrate this relativity of simultaneity, we shall outline a well-known thought experiment.[9] A train is moving along a station platform. A conductor C is on the train, a station-master M sits on the platform. Let the relative velocity of the train with respect to the platform be v. The stationmaster has placed mirrors at A and B. When the conductor C is coincident with M, M sends out a light pulse. He notices that its reflections from A and B return to him coincidently; in accordance with stipulation (28), he regards the two reflections as simultaneous.

Of course, the reflections do not return coincidently to the conductor, who has moved a bit in the meantime. (He is moving toward B; hence, the reflection from B reaches him before it reaches M. By the same token, the reflection from A will reach him after having passed M. Since these two reflections coincide at M, the latter reaches the conductor after the former.) So in accordance with stipulation (28), the conductor concludes that the two reflections are not simultaneous. The two reflections are simultaneous in the frame in which M is regarded as at rest; they are not simultaneous in the frame in which C is regarded as at rest—given, of course, the definition of "simultaneous" by means of Einstein's stipulation (28).

4. Duration in the Special Theory of Relativity

a. Clocks and Duration

By definition, what a clock measures is *duration* (quantity of time). But of what does it measure the duration? As Leibniz already pointed out, measurement is *directly* of the relevant quantity in an entity coincident with the instrument. So if a clock is rigidly affixed to a body, then it certainly measures the duration of a process in that body or to which that body is subject. For example, suppose that a car is equipped with both an odometer and a clock. If we wish to know the distance covered by the car during a given journey, we note the initial and final readings of the odometer. If we wish to know the duration of the journey, we note the initial and final readings of the clock. Of course, this is not only the duration of the journey made by the car but also the duration of the journey made by the clock. So the clock measures the duration of any process to which it is itself subject, and in addition, that of any process undergone by a body with which it remains coincident during that process. (Note that *during* is a concept of temporal order; in addition, the notion of simultaneity between spatially separate events is not involved in our discussion.)

In classical physics it is furthermore assumed that a clock measures the duration of any other process with which it is in coincidence at the beginning *and* at the end. Thus, suppose that the car goes from New York to New Haven and that the clock is detached and flown to New Haven, where it is present at the arrival of the car. Then from the classical point of view, its initial and final readings also determine the duration of the car's journey.

Given the clock postulate, however, we cannot consistently make this assumption. For this postulate entails that clocks moved the same distance at different speeds will not agree. Of course, we need not retain the Leibnizian notion that the clock which remains with the car gives the "uniquely true" measure of the journey's duration. We may simply say that the duration relative to the one clock is such and such, and the duration relative to the other clock is so and so. Clocks in relative motion with respect to each other simply do not agree. But as a matter of terminology, the readings of the clock in the car are said to measure the "proper time" of the processes to which the car (or the clock itself) is subject. What we wish to discuss now is how the readings of clocks in motion relative to each other are related. To do this, we shall have to be more explicit on the subject of frames of reference.

b. Frames of Reference

A frame of reference is simply an assignment of time and space coordinates to all events. This assignment must of course respect, first of all, the temporal and spatial order relations among these events. Second, we must be concerned about the metric. In the special theory of relativity, space is assumed to be Euclidean, so there must be a certain agreement between what yardsticks show and the distance formula

$$(29) \quad d(X,Y) = \sqrt{(x_1 - x_2)^2 + (y_1 - y_2)^2 + (z_1 - z_2)^2}$$

where X and Y have the spatial coordinates (x_1, y_1, z_1) and (x_2, y_2, z_2), respectively. Finally, in the special theory of relativity we are concerned only with *inertial systems*—that is, if such a distance measurement is made in a system, it concerns us only provided the system is free from those force effects that Newton thought revealed absolute acceleration.

We shall now describe a specific frame of reference S. It is the frame that belongs to a particular inertial system A. Rigidly attached to A is a standard clock C. The family of standard clocks we shall not define. Of course, we assume that any two standard clocks are equivalent in the usual sense that if they are synchronized, they then remain synchronized for as long as they remain coincident. We draw a line (*world line*) to represent the history of A (see Figure 3).

In S, every event E has coordinates (t,x,y,z), t being its date or time coordinate and x, y, and z its space coordinates. The system A is at rest in S, so every event involving A has the same space coordinates. We choose A as the spatial origin—that is, each event involving A has the space coordinates $(0,0,0)$. Of course, the time coordinate of such an event is the reading of the clock C coincident with that event. The reading 0 of C marks the *origin* of the frame of reference, $(0,0,0,0)$.

To determine the date of an event not involving A, we shall use Einstein's stipulation (28) and formula (26). Thus, if the emission of a light signal has coordinates $(0,0,0,0)$ and its return to A has $(2t,0,0,0)$, then the time coordinate of its reflection Y is t. To determine the spatial distance of Y from A (rather, from the event W involving A which also has time coordinate t), we need a further convention. This convention is simply that the speed of light will be used as a unit: $c = 1$. The distance in question is, of course, half the time interval of the round trip of the signal, divided by c:

$$d(Y,W) = \frac{1}{2}\left(\frac{2t - 0}{c}\right) = \frac{t}{c}$$

which, due to our convention is just t. Choosing the X-T plane to pass through Y, its spatial coordinates are $(x,0,0)$ with $x = t$.

Of course, this method of measuring distances by means of a clock and light signals cannot be guaranteed a priori to yield the same results as those of measuring rods. That this is nevertheless so in an inertial system is asserted by the special theory of relativity.[10]

c. The Duration Postulate

To determine the relationships among moving clocks, we consider two inertial frames S and S'. Let S be defined by the body A and clock C (in the sense used in Section 4b) and S' by body A' and clock C'. In frame S we measure the velocity of A'; say it is v. (Of course, the velocity of A in S is just 0, so the relative velocity of A and A' in S is v.) For convenience, we suppose that A' remains in the X-T plane of system S. We postulate that the velocity of A' in S is constant, so that its path in S is a straight line.

To begin, we suppose that A and A' are in coincidence exactly when their clocks C and C' both read *zero*. In other words, the coordinates $(0,0,0,0)$ are assigned to the same events in both systems. We shall draw the X- and T-axes of the system S, and also the world line of the body A' (which is, of course, the T'-axis of system S': see Figure 3). The body A emits a light signal (event E) that is reflected from A' (event Z) and returns to A (event F). What is the time coordinate $t = t(Z)$ of Z in the system S? By formulas (26) and (28) we find:

(30) $\quad t = t(E) + \frac{1}{2}(t(F) - t(E))$

Let us introduce the symbol d to denote half the time interval (by clock C) between E and F:

(31) $\quad d = \frac{1}{2}(t(F) - t(E))$

Then we have:

(32) $\quad \begin{aligned} t(E) &= t - d \\ t(F) &= t + d \\ t(Z) &= t \end{aligned}$

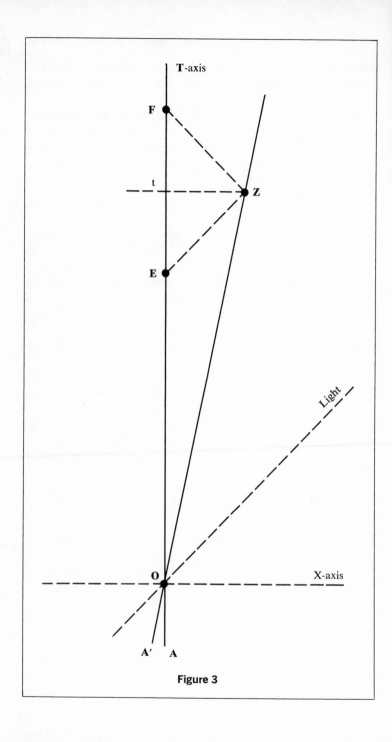

Figure 3

We have stipulated that body A' moves only along the X-axis (its world line is entirely in the X-T plane). Therefore, the spatial coordinates of Z are x, 0, 0 for some value of x. What is this value? Well, the light signal traveled at speed $c = 1$ for an interval $t - (t - d) = d$ to reach A' (path E to Z). Therefore, the distance is $d/c = d/1 = d$. The coordinates of Z are therefore $(t,d,0,0)$.

Now we can calculate the velocity v by which A' moves relative to A. At time 0, A' was in coincidence with A (distance zero). At time t, it had moved to a point at a distance d from A. Hence, in the amount of time $(t - 0)$ it moved a distance $(d - 0)$. Its velocity therefore equals

(33) $v = \dfrac{d}{t}$, or $d = vt$

The question we now wish to have answered is: What is the reading of the other clock C' when it is coincident with Z? (In other words, what is the time coordinate t' of Z in the system S'?) This is an empirical question, which cannot be answered on the basis of our previous postulates.

The answer given by the special theory of relativity may be expressed as follows:

(34) *Duration postulate* A clock measures the space-time intervals along its own world line.

Since C' reads 0 when it is coincident with 0 and t' when it is coincident with Z, this means that $t' - 0 = t'$ equals the magnitude of the space-time interval between 0 and Z. As measured in the system S, that interval has the magnitude $\sqrt{t^2 - d^2}$. So for the case illustrated in Figure 3, the duration postulate means that

(35) $t' = \sqrt{t^2 - d^2}$

which, recalling (33), is the same as $t\sqrt{1 - v^2}$. Since $c = 1$ by our conventions, this consequence coincides with the Lorentz time-dilation hypothesis (see Section 2b).

Note that the postulate would lead to contradiction if space-time intervals along world lines had different values in different frames of reference. The postulate says that the magnitude of such an interval between two points on a single world line (of an inertial system) is the same in each frame of reference. The more general invariance assertion—that the magnitude of *any* space-time interval is the same in all frames of reference—follows from the Lorentz transformations, which we deduce in Section 5.

Figure 3, however, illustrates only one situation: the case in which C and C' are not at rest relative to each other. If they are at rest relative to each other, but apart spatially, their world lines never intersect. Hence, we cannot find an event O belonging to both world lines that will serve as the origin for both frames of reference. In that case, how is t' related to t? Let signals be emitted from A (events E and F) to arrive at A' (events Y and Z); let $t(Y) = t$ and $t(Z) = t + a$. What the duration postulate says here is that $|t'(Z) - t'(Y)|$ equals the magnitude of the spatiotemporal interval between Y and Z. As measured in system S, that magnitude is

$$\sqrt{(t + a - t)^2 - (d - d)^2} = \sqrt{a^2} = a$$

In other words,

$$|t'(Z) - t'(Y)| = |t(Z) - t(Y)|$$

for any two events Y and Z on the world line of the clock C'. If we assume that the two clocks agree on the "direction" of time (i.e., $t(Y) < t(Z)$ if and only if $t'(Y) < t'(Z)$), then this can also be expressed by saying

There is a constant factor k such that, for any event X on the world line of C', $t'(X) = t(X) + k$.

Then we can say that C and C' are synchronized if and only if this factor equals zero.

5. The Lorentz Transformations as a Consequence of Einstein's Assumptions[11]

A proper time interval along the world line of a body is measured by a clock rigidly attached to that body. In Figure 3, we see three such proper time intervals marked: OE, OF, and OZ.

(The first and second are measured by clock C, and the third by clock C'.) Because E, Z, and F are the emission, reflection, and return of a light signal, we shall designate them as follows:

(OE) first interval of emission
(OZ) first interval of reception
(OZ) second interval of emission
(OF) second interval of reception

This terminology is used because so far as present considerations are concerned, Z might as well be the reception of one signal (emission E) as the emission of a second signal (reception F). We shall try to show that the ratio of interval of reception to interval of emission is the same for both cases. Since O has the time coordinate 0 in all cases, this means:

(36) *Lemma 1* $t'(Z) \div t(E) = t(F) \div t'(Z)$

Using the conventions of Section 4c ($t(E) = t - d$, $t(F) = t + d$, $t(Z) = t$), this means:

(37) $\dfrac{t'}{t - d} = \dfrac{t + d}{t'}$

That is just the same as

(38) $(t')^2 = (t + d)(t - d)$

hence the same as

(39) $(t')^2 = t^2 - d^2$

But of course, (39) follows directly from the duration postulate, (34); hence, our lemma is proved.

Now we shall prove that this ratio is a function only of the relative velocity v. This means that it will be the same *for any one-way signal* sent from A to A' or from A' to A.

(40) *Lemma 2* $\dfrac{t'(Z)}{t(E)} = \dfrac{\sqrt{1 + v}}{\sqrt{1 - v}}$

Again using our conventions, we can express this as

(41) $\dfrac{t'}{t - d} = \dfrac{\sqrt{1 + v}}{\sqrt{1 - v}}$

The postulate of duration allows us to express the left-hand side as

(42) $\dfrac{t'}{t-d} = \dfrac{\sqrt{t^2-d^2}}{t-d} = \dfrac{\sqrt{(t-d)(t+d)}}{t-d}$

hence,

(43) $\dfrac{t'}{t-d} = \dfrac{\sqrt{t+d}}{\sqrt{t-d}}$

Now we use our previous result, (33), to express d as vt, thus rewriting the right-hand side of (43)

(44) $\dfrac{t'}{t-d} = \dfrac{\sqrt{t+vt}}{\sqrt{t-vt}} = \dfrac{\sqrt{t(1+v)}}{\sqrt{t(1-v)}}$

Canceling the factor $\sqrt{t}$ on the right-hand side, we deduce (41); thus, our second lemma is proved. These two lemmas will make the deduction of the Lorentz transformations very simple.[12]

As usual, we shall focus our attention on events in the X-T plane, so that we have at once the transformations

$y' = y$
$z' = z$

This lack of generality will only avoid inessential complications. Let us then consider an event W with coordinates (t,x,y,z) in S and (t',x',y',z') in S'. We also draw the paths of light signals that connect A, A' and W (see Figure 4). By convention we introduce two symbols d and d' just as before, so that we have:

(45) $d = \frac{1}{2}(t(F_1) - t(E_1))$
$d' = \frac{1}{2}(t'(F_2) - t'(E_2))$
$t(E_1) = t - d$
$t(F_1) = t + d$
$t'(E_2) = t' - d'$
$t'(F_2) = t' + d'$

And just as before we deduce the spatial distance of W from A, and from A', and hence its spatial coordinates

(46) $x = d$
$x' = d'$

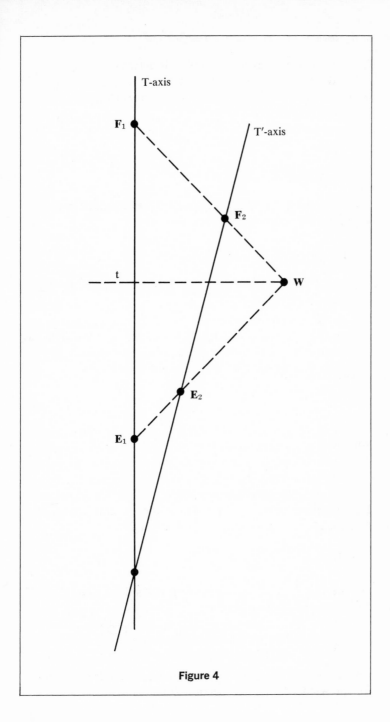

Figure 4

Our task is now to express t' and x' in terms of t and x.

We do this by using lemmas (1) and (2) concerning the ratio of interval of reception to interval of emission:

For signal E_1E_2: $\quad \dfrac{t'(E_2)}{t(E_1)} = \dfrac{\sqrt{1 + v}}{\sqrt{1 - v}}$

For signal F_2F_1: $\quad \dfrac{t(F_1)}{t'(F_2)} = \dfrac{\sqrt{1 + v}}{\sqrt{1 - v}}$

Using (45) and (46) these equalities can be expressed equivalently as

(47) $t' - x' = (t - x)\dfrac{\sqrt{1 + v}}{\sqrt{1 - v}}$

(48) $t' + x' = (t + x)\dfrac{\sqrt{1 - v}}{\sqrt{1 + v}}$

Adding the quantities on either side of the equality signs, we obtain:

(49) $(t' - x') + (t' + x')$

$\quad = (t - x)\dfrac{\sqrt{1 + v}}{\sqrt{1 - v}} + (t + x)\dfrac{\sqrt{1 - v}}{\sqrt{1 + v}}$

which is just

(50) $2t' = \dfrac{2t - 2xv}{\sqrt{1 - v^2}}$

Dividing both sides by 2 we obtain the Lorentz transformation for the time coordinate (see Section 2c)

(51) $t' = \dfrac{t - xv}{\sqrt{1 - v^2}}$

On the other hand, by subtracting the sides of equality (47) from those of (48), we obtain:

(52) $2x' = (t + x)\dfrac{\sqrt{1 - v}}{\sqrt{1 + v}} - (t - x)\dfrac{\sqrt{1 + v}}{\sqrt{1 - v}}$

which, after division by 2 yields the Lorentz transformation for the X-coordinate (see Section 2c)

(53) $x' = \dfrac{x - vt}{\sqrt{1 - v^2}}$

Thus, we have shown that the Lorentz transformations can be deduced from the duration postulate (in the context of Einstein's other assumptions).

6. Space-Time and the Minkowski Diagram

In the classic treatment of space, each event received a triple (x,y,z) of real numbers as its space coordinates. Therefore, the logical space in which, classically, all spatial relationships are represented, is the set of all triples of real numbers. The assignment of coordinates involves, of course, the choice of an origin and a choice of units, as well as of the orientation of the X-axis, and so on. In other words, it involves the choice of a spatial frame of reference.

We have now been following the procedure of assigning each event a quadruple (t,x,y,z) of real numbers as its *space-time coordinates*. Thus, the logical space in which, for us, all *spatiotemporal* relationships are represented is the set of all quadruples of real numbers. An assignment of space-time coordinates involves the choice of a total frame of reference, and we are focusing our attention only on those for which this choice is an inertial frame. In addition, we have stipulated that the coordinatizations should satisfy Einstein's convention $\varepsilon = 1/2$ and the convention (for units of measurement) that $c = 1$.

The various magnitudes that may be measured in a given frame of reference may be the same in all frames (invariant) or different from frame to frame (relative). For example, two events that are separate spatially may be simultaneous in one frame and not in another. We illustrated this with the story of the conductor and the stationmaster (*relativity of simultaneity*). The most important invariant magnitude is the space-time interval s between two events. This interval is given by the equation $s^2 = t^2 - d^2$, where t is the difference between the times of the two events, and d the spatial distance between them. Here t and d are measured in a given frame S, and we

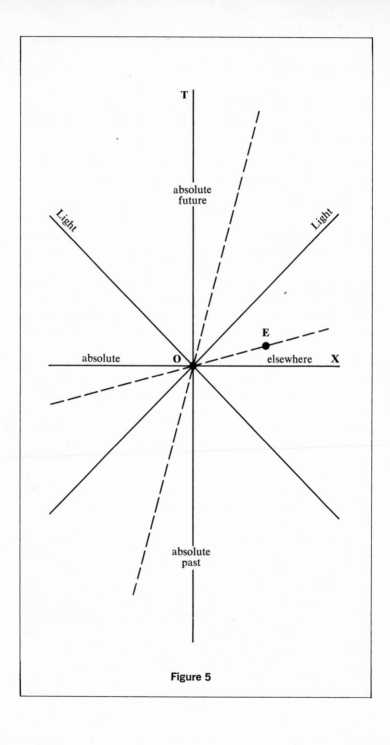

Figure 5

know that simultaneity is relative, so the magnitude of t will vary from frame to frame. But the magnitude of s will not vary. This has the immediate corollary that the magnitude d varies from frame to frame (*relativity of length*).

Spatiotemporal relationships may be depicted in a *Minkowski diagram*.[13] The events in the history of a body A are represented by the points on a vertical (solid) line, the *world line* of A. This world line also provides the time axis of A's frame of reference. We choose some point on it as origin and draw a horizontal line through it to represent one of the spatial dimensions. Light rays coincident with that origin appear as (solid) lines at a 45° angle to these axes. The broken lines represent the time and space axes of another frame of reference in motion with respect to A's frame.

The light rays through the point O divide the diagram into three regions: *absolute future, absolute past,* and *absolute elsewhere* (see Figure 5). The region absolute elsewhere can be characterized in two ways:

(a) E is in the absolute elsewhere of O if and only if it is impossible for any signal to have its departure coincident with E and arrival coincident with O, or vice versa.

(b) E is in the absolute elsewhere of O if and only if the square of the space-time interval between E and O is negative.

Here (a) expresses the limiting nature of the velocity of light. On the other hand, (b) defines the region in terms of the invariant relationship given by the space-time interval. It says that $|d|$ is greater than $|t|$ for such events: their separation is *spacelike*. To put it another way: there is some alternative frame of reference S' such that O and E both lie on the X'-axis (are simultaneous in S').

The absolute past and absolute future constitute the *light cone* of O. An event in the light cone of O has a *timelike* separation from O—that is, for some alternative system S', they happen in the same place but not at the same time. Furthermore, there is *no* alternative system S' in which that event and O are simultaneous.

Chapter VI

The Causal
Theory
of Time and
Space-Time

As we have already noted, at the end of the nineteenth century, the great problem in the theory of time was the problem of temporal order—of providing a theory that would exhibit the physical basis for temporal relations. There was a similar problem for the theory of space, but it seemed reasonable to expect that such an account in terms of the behavior of light rays and material bodies could be made precise, given only a precise theory of time order and the necessary effort.

1. The Philosophy of
Time and Space
in the Twentieth Century

The advent of the theory of relativity drastically changed the conception of these problems, but at the same time it provided the necessary clues—and the stimulus—for their solution. We cannot hope to recount the whole story of the philosophy of time and space in our century in one short chapter. Instead, in this section we shall give an outline of the most important developments and in the remainder of the chapter we shall follow only a single strand, which leads to a solution to these problems.

One of the first to attempt a comprehensive analysis of temporal, spatial, and spatiotemporal relations within the special theory of relativity was Alfred A. Robb. At the same time as Einstein and Robb, Whitehead was developing a comprehensive theory of time and space, which was, however, in basic disagreement with Einstein's critique of simultaneity. Russell had attempted a thorough logical analysis of the foundations of (classical) physics in his *Principles of Mathematics* (1903). His views on time and space as developed there are basically Newtonian. He became converted to a relational theory of time and space through the influence of Whitehead and published it in *Our Knowledge of the External World* (1914). Whitehead published his own theory in three books on natural philosophy (1919–1922). By this time Whitehead had developed a theory of relativity that was an alternative to Einstein's and apparently not in conflict with the observational data.[1] It seems that Russell came to agree more with Einstein; in any case, his analysis of space-time structure in *The Analysis of Matter* (1927) concerns the foundations of Einstein's theory of relativity. Here Russell mentions explicitly a debt to the work of Robb.

While Robb, Whitehead, and Russell were engaged in a philosophical and logical analysis of the theory of relativity and space-time structure in England, the rapidly growing school of logical empiricism (or logical positivism) was doing so on the Continent. Here we must mention especially Moritz Schlick, Carnap, Reichenbach, and Henryk Mehlberg. The logical empiricists have the reputation of being decidedly ahistorical, but in this case the reputation does not seem deserved. Like their English colleagues, they studied the work of Poincaré as well as Einstein; and furthermore, the work of Helmholtz and Mach. Reichenbach wrote a book concerning Kant's theory of time and space—*Relativity and A Priori*

Knowledge (1920)—and a paper on Leibniz's theory and his debate with the Newtonians.[2] Russell's writings were extensively studied among the logical positivists; also, Carnap mentions Whitehead's theory of space-time structure in connection with an exposition of his own.[3] Mehlberg's encyclopedic *Essai sur la théorie causale du temps* (1935–1937) includes lengthy discussions of Newton, Leibniz, Kant, and Lechalas, as well as the later writers.

Reichenbach became the major philosopher of science to write on the philosophy of time and space, with the publication of *Axiomatik der relativistischen Raum-Zeit-Lehre* (1924), *The Philosophy of Space and Time* (1928; English translation, 1958), and *The Direction of Time* (1956). His work was continued by Grünbaum in *Philosophical Problems of Space and Time* (1963) and *Modern Science and Zeno's Paradoxes* (1967).

2. Reichenbach's Causal Theory of Time Order

We can distinguish roughly between an early formulation and a later formulation of Reichenbach's theory. The former is developed in *Axiomatik der relativistischen Raum-Zeit-Lehre*[4] and in *The Philosophy of Space and Time,* the latter in his posthumously published work *The Direction of Time.*

a. The Early Formulation

To define the temporal order of events, Reichenbach introduced several basic relations among events. The first is *genidentity:* E is genidentical with E' if they involve the same object. The second is causation. A light signal, for example, is a *causal chain,* because in Reichenbach's terminology the emission of such a signal is one of the causes of its eventual reflections and final absorption; each reflection is also one of the causes of later reflections and final absorption.

In *The Philosophy of Space and Time,* Reichenbach introduces his theory of time order with the following passage:

> If E_2 is the effect of E_1, then E_2 is called *later than* E_1. This is the topological coordinative definition of time order.[5]

Of course, the italicized sentence does not have the correct form for a definition of "is later than." Nor should it: certainly, it is possible for some event E to be later than E_1 without being one of its effects. But the definition will do for all those pairs of events that are causally connected, that is, that belong to the same causal chain. In the *Axiomatik* we find a more general definition, which amounts to

(1) E_2 is *later* than E_1 if and only if it is physically possible for there to be a chain $s_1, s_2, \ldots, s_k$ such that for each i, from 1 to $k - 1$, s_i is a cause of s_{i+1}; and such that E_1 coincides with s_1 and E_2 with s_k.[6]

This general definition makes use of three basic concepts: *causation, coincidence,* and *physical possibility.*

We must carefully distinguish two senses of "coincides" here:

(a) (spatial) coincidence among bodies (body A_1 coincides with body A_2 at time t)
(b) (spatiotemporal) coincidence among events (event E_1 coincides with event E_2)

In (1), "coincides" has sense (b); thus, one of Reichenbach's basic concepts is a spatiotemporal concept. (Note that sense [b] cannot be defined in terms of sense [a].)

The use of "physically possible" refers to the limiting nature of the velocity of light. Some pairs of events belonging to different world lines cannot be connected by a causal chain, because such a connection would be tantamount to a signal faster than light. Hence, the following defined relation only partially correlates the temporal order of events on different world lines:

(2) E_1 and E_2 are *indeterminate as to time order* if and only if neither is later than the other.

Hence, as we saw in Chapter V, there is a certain amount of arbitrariness in the assignment of time coordinates, even with respect to order. But we can lay down the exact conditions under which a coordinate assignment reflects the topological relationships induced by possible connections through causal chains:

> (3) An assignment t of real numbers to events is a *topologically admissible coordinatization* if and only if
> (a) if E_1 and E_2 coincide, $t(E_1) = t(E_2)$;
> (b) if E_2 is later than E_1, $t(E_1) < t(E_2)$

This has as consequence that if E_1 and E_2 do not coincide, $t(E_1) = t(E_2)$ only if E_1 and E_2 are indeterminate as to time order. It also means that any two admissible coordinate assignments will agree for the order of events on the same world line—at least, Reichenbach assumes that if E_1 and E_2 are genidentical, then they either coincide or are causally connectible. Finally, note that Reichenbach is clearly assuming that time is topologically open—that is, that there are no closed causal chains. This is an assumption that he discusses and that he says is empirically well confirmed, though not logically necessary.

The major criticisms of this theory center on Reichenbach's use of the notion of *cause*. Since Hume, no philosopher can afford an uncritical use of this notion. But even if one takes the view that the notion of causal connection is prephilosophical and that the question is not whether there are causal connections but how they are correctly described, Reichenbach faces a problem. For he relies explicitly on the asymmetry of such connections, on the distinction between cause and effect. If he wishes to say, like Leibniz, that by definition the "earlier" one of a causally connected pair is the cause, then he must provide a criterion for distinguishing the cause from the effect.

Reichenbach recognized this problem and attempted to provide such a criterion. He gave this criterion—now usually called the *mark method*—the following formulation:

> *If* E_1 *is the cause of* E_2, *then a small variation* (a mark) *in* E_1 *is associated with a small variation in* E_2, *whereas small variations in* E_2 *are not associated with variations in* E_1.[7]

Suppose for example that I throw a stone across a creek. Let E_1 be the event of my throwing the stone and E_2 the event of the stone landing on the other side of the creek. If we mark the stone with chalk during event E_1, a chalk mark will be present on the stone during event E_2. But if we mark the stone with chalk during E_2, it does not follow that a chalk mark appears on the stone during E_1. From this we may infer, by Reichenbach's criterion, that E_1 is the cause and E_2 the effect.

The mark method was extensively—and I think conclusively —criticized by Mehlberg and Grünbaum.[8] The criticisms attempt to establish that a tacit use is made of concepts of time order in the use of the mark method. The most important of these criticisms is that the marking process used must be irreversible: if, for example, the chalk can be rubbed off at some point on the stone's trajectory that links E_1 and E_2, the criterion does not work. But when is a marking process irreversible? When its effect (the mark) cannot be destroyed or deleted without destroying the subject or giving the subject some other mark, which means that the subject cannot exist in the state preceding the marking at some time after the marking. There seems to be no way of distinguishing irreversible and reversible marking processes without using the notion of *later,* or *temporally between,* or some similar notion of temporal order. Hence, the mark method cannot be used in the definition or explication of (the whole of) temporal order.

Although this is the major criticism of Reichenbach's early theory, it is also important to point out that his use of the notion of spatiotemporal coincidence limits that theory. It was Reichenbach's avowed aim to give a purely causal or physical account of space-time; yet one of his primitive relations is a spatiotemporal relation.

b. The Later Formulation

In his later work, Reichenbach distinguished clearly between time order and the anisotrophy of time (what he called the "direction" of time). The relation *is later than* was henceforth to be defined in terms of temporal betweenness and certain factual asymmetries in actual (betweenness-ordered) series of events. The reader is already familiar with this point of view from our discussion in Chapter III, Section 3.

What we must explore, then, is Reichenbach's later account (in *The Direction of Time*) of temporal betweenness. As before, Reichenbach regards genidentity as a species of causal

connection and also calls the emission, absorption, and intermediate reflections of a light signal genidentical with each
other. Besides genidentity, *approximate spatiotemporal coincidence* is a basic notion. There are two further basic notions
that we shall mention shortly.

With our attention restricted to genidentity (and signal)
relations (as opposed to causal connections in general), we
can introduce the derivative notion of a *causal net,* so called
because it can be drawn like a net. Lines in the net represent
genidentity chains, and knots in the net represent spatiotemporal coincidences among events. As before, Reichenbach says that closed causal chains ("time travel") may be
ruled out on empirical grounds. He does admit here the possibility of closed time, though this possibility is not reflected in
the formulation of the theory.

On a single world line ("genidentity chain," "causal chain")
the events are ordered by the relation of approximate coincidence. If X is an event on world line W, let us call U a *neigh-
borhood* of X if it contains X, and all members of U are in
approximate coincidence with X. Then if U_1, U_2, U_3 are
neighborhoods of X_1, X_2, and X_3, and U_1 overlaps U_2, U_2
overlaps U_3, and U_3 does not overlap U_1, then X_2 is *between*
X_1 and X_3. We may call this relation among X_1, X_2, X_3—the
having of neighborhoods, thus related—*local betweenness.*
Betweenness simpliciter on the world line can be defined in
terms of local betweenness.

Within a knot we may also find cases of local betweenness,
which correlate the order on several world lines with each
other. The easiest way to use approximate coincidence to
order a whole causal net is simply to assign each event X a
coordinate $t(X)$ such that

(4) If Y, but not Z, is in approximate coincidence with X,
then $t(Y)$ should be numerically closer to $t(X)$ than
$t(Z)$ is:

$$|t(X) - t(Y)| < |t(X) - t(Z)|$$

Then numerical betweenness among the coordinates can be
used to define betweenness among the events.

But this immediately shows up an important problem, which

leads to the introduction of a further basic notion. Suppose that of all the events on world line W, only X is in approximate coincidence with some event (say X') on world line W' (see Figure 6). Then we have no way of deciding, by the criterion above, between the following two kinds of coordinate assignment:

(I) $t(X) = t(X')$ (II) $t(X) = t(X')$
    $t(Y) = t(Y')$ $t(Y) = t(Z')$
    $t(Z) = t(Z')$ $t(Z) = t(Y')$

As we have drawn the picture it would seem that assignment (I) is correct and (II) incorrect. But up to this point in Reichenbach's account we have no objective basis for distinguishing between the represented situation and the alternative possible situation in which the processes $Z'X'Y'$ and ZXY are "counterdirected." Reichenbach's solution is to introduce the concept of *local comparability of time order*. Whatever the exact reconstruction of this concept, it allows us to distinguish the two kinds of situations represented by coordinate assignments (I) and (II).

Even now, however, the set of basic notions is not sufficient. For if it is merely *possible* for some world line or causal chain to have some of its (noncoincident) members coincide with X and Y, then X and Y are temporally separate. The mere fact that *actually* X and Y are not thus connected does not entail that they are indeterminate as to time order; for this they are to be *not connectible*. Hence, Reichenbach introduces as final basic notion that of being *possibly connected* by a causal chain (causally connectible).

Reichenbach's later theory is certainly an improvement on his earlier theory. Yet we can point out some features that are not entirely satisfactory. To start with the least important one, the fourth basic relation (causal connectibility) makes the third (local comparability) redundant. To show that the situation is as represented by (I) rather than (II) it would be sufficient to point out, for example, that Y and Z', but not Y and Y' are causally connectible (see the dotted lines in Figure 6). We may also point out that, just as in the early theory, use is made of an irreducibly spatiotemporal relation (approximate spatio-

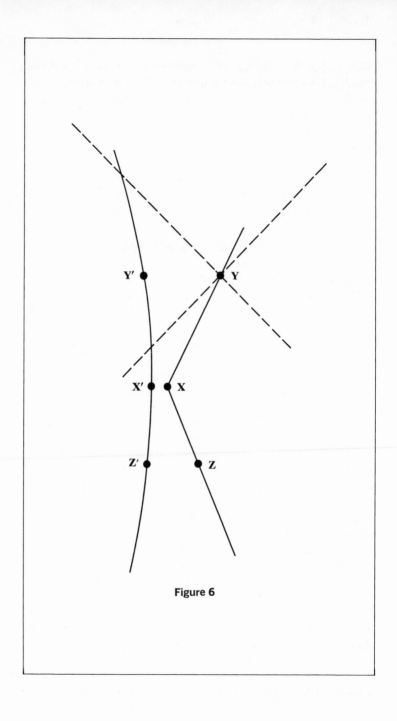

Figure 6

temporal coincidence). Finally, the formulation of the theory given by Reichenbach does not apply directly to the case of closed time.

3. Grünbaum's Causal Theory of Time Order

In *Philosophical Problems of Space and Time,* Grünbaum decided to take explicitly into account the possibility that time is topologically closed.[9] He also eliminated the use of a primitive notion of spatiotemporal coincidence. But his formulation of the theory encountered certain difficulties, and he offered a new formulation in *Modern Science and Zeno's Paradoxes.*

a. The First Formulation

The basic notions used by Grünbaum in his first account were those of *genidentity, physical necessity* (or physical possibility— these two notions are interdefinable), and *k-connection.* Two events are *k*-connected if they are genidentical or are an emission, absorption, or reflection of the same light signal; or if they are coincident with two thus connected events. (Note that the last explanation is only a heuristic comment; in the theory itself, "coincidence" would be defined in terms of "*k*-connection," not vice versa.) So except for the terminology, his basic notions are essentially those used by Reichenbach (except for "coincidence"). Grünbaum's definition of "topologically simultaneous" shows that this is exactly what Reichenbach meant by "indeterminate as to time order."

(5) Events X and Y are *topologically simultaneous* if and only if it is physically necessary that X and Y are not k-connected.

Besides these similarities, we also find that Grünbaum had adopted Reichenbach's basic strategy: to define temporal order on each world line individually and to correlate the separate orderings by means of topological simultaneity.

The basic difference between Grünbaum and Reichenbach

appears in Grünbaum's definition of temporal relations on a given world line. First, Grünbaum does not use coincidence for this purpose. Second, he defines pair separation rather than betweenness, in order to cover the case of closed time. His definition uses the notation "$n(E\ L\ E'\ M)$," which may be read as "events E and E' are temporally separated by L and M."

(6) $n(E\ L\ E'\ M)$ if and only if $E \neq E'$, L and M are genidentical with E and E', and, given the actual occurrence of E and E', it is physically necessary that either L or M occur in order that E and E' be k-connected.

If the world line is open, betweenness can be defined in terms of separation.

At first sight, the use of the notion of physical necessity in (6) cannot be objectionable if we accept its use in (5) as correct (as Reichenbach certainly had). But in fact, the modal construction in (6) is much more complicated than in (5) and leads to certain difficult questions of interpretation. In *Philosophical Problems of Space and Time* Grünbaum discusses an objection raised by Abner Shimony.[10] Let us suppose that time is open, and X occurs between B and C, but A not between B and C, all on the same world line. For simplicity, let us suppose that A occurs before B, B before X, X before C. It now appears that Grünbaum must hold that if X had not occurred, B and C would not be genidentical. This is certainly so if X is simply "deleted," but what if another event had occurred in the place of X?

To give an example, suppose I wake up, shave, and go to work. Then on Grünbaum's account, my shaving is temporally second in this sequence, because if I had not shaved, my waking and my going to work would not be k-connected (hence, not genidentical). This is certainly so if my not shaving prevents me from going to work, in which case the third event would not have happened at all. But I might simply have trimmed my beard instead of shaving it off and gone to work defying the bourgeois fashion.

An answer to this criticism would be that we are assuming a perfectly deterministic universe so that, given two events ("total states") on a world line, the rest is fixed. (This also requires the world line to be one of an isolated system, of course; also, it must be time-reversible determinism, since we are really concerned with *between,* not with *before.*) But if we assume such determinism, then if A does not occur on the world line, this may be either because the system ceases to exist then (so that B and C do not exist either) or because another event A' occurs in its place. In the latter case, B and C cannot both occur also, for the possibility of both sequences ABC and $A'BC$ contradicts the assumed determinism. The conclusion would be that the occurrence of A is also necessary for the k-connection of B and C; hence, by Grünbaum's definition, A is also between B and C.

Grünbaum first attempted to answer this further criticism by drawing a distinction between "necessary for the occurrence of" and "necessary for the k-connection of," and this was indeed an adequate answer to the objection as first presented. When the question is raised (as we have done) whether the world is deterministic or indeterministic, this distinction no longer disarms the objection. Grünbaum saw this very well, of course, and hence worked out a second formulation.

b. The Second Formulation

In the second formulation of his causal theory of time, Grünbaum used the notion of physical necessity only in the definition of topological simultaneity—that is, this modal notion appears only in the use of the concept of a pair of *causally (non)connectible* events. He also uses the notions of genidentity and k-connection again. Finally, he now assumes that the *spatial ordering* of events is given.[11] In the context of special relativity, this may be taken to be the space of some inertial frame of reference or other.

We shall now use the notation "$dn(E\ X\ E'\ F)$" for "X and F temporally separate E' and E." The definition proceeds in two steps. Let E, X, E', and F be distinct events on a *spatially nonself-intersecting* world line W.

(7) The set K of events on a world line W continuously k-connects E and E' if and only if

(a) E and E' belong to K, and
(b) the spatial positions of the members of K form a continuum.
(8) $dn(E \; X \; E' \; F)$ if and only if every class K that continuously k-connects E and E' on W is such that either X or F belongs to K.

This gives the temporal order on spatially nonself-intersecting world lines; the relation of topological simultaneity can then be used to "transfer" this order to other world lines.

This revision certainly removes the last difficulty with the causal theory of time order. It is to be granted, however, that this has been done at the cost of assuming a certain spatial ordering of events as given. There is, as far as we know, no independent explication of this spatial order that could be used to extend this theory of time order into a complete causal theory of spatiotemporal order. Thus, the hope of a complete explication of space-time in terms of physical relations among events is here renounced.

It is not a requirement of a theory of time that it be also a theory of space or of space-time. Thus, it cannot be an objection to Grünbaum's account of temporal order that it appeals to spatial relations among events (especially as this account occurs in a discussion of Zeno's paradoxes, and the published account does not claim to present a comprehensive theory of time order, but only of the denseness of this order). In Section 4, however, we shall find that the theory is capable of a significant *simplification* and that in this simplified form it no longer relies on any purely spatial or spatiotemporal concepts.

4. Systematic Exposition of the Causal Theory of Time Order

In the formulations of the theory of time order by Reichenbach and Grünbaum we can discern a single basic strategy. This strategy consists in *first* explicating the time order of the events on a single world line and *then* explicating the time order of all events by correlating the world lines (through the relation of causal connectibility). If we wish to cover the case of a universe in which only one continuant exists—in which case there would be only one world line—this strategy is the only possible one. But in fact, the aims of a theory of time do not make it essential that this case is covered.

This suggests an alternative strategy: explication of the time order of events on any world line (in part) through their relations to events on other world lines.[12] This is the strategy that we shall adopt here; it leads to a basic simplification of the theory. The primitive terms we shall need are common to all the formulations that we have examined thus far: event, genidentity, and causal connectibility. As before, we shall restrict our attention to events that involve a single body. We shall not regard a light signal as a body; its emission and absorption are causally connected, but not genidentical with each other in our sense.

As in our account of Reichenbach's and Grünbaum's formulations of the theory, we shall proceed by giving definitions. The reader is now quite familiar with the notion of a definition's presuppositions; he will see that our postulates are postulates of adequacy for our definitions, and are intended to guarantee these presuppositions.

Postulate I Genidentity is an equivalence relation (reflexive, symmetric, and transitive; binary) among events.

Definition 1 A *world line* is a class W of events any two of which are genidentical with each other, such that any event not in W is not genidentical with all the members of W.

Here we call a relation among events *binary* if it always relates a pair of events, *reflexive* if every event bears the relation to itself, or *symmetric* if the following holds:

If X bears the relation to Y, then Y bears the relation to X.

and *transitive* if the following holds:

If X bears the relation to Y, and Y bears the relation to Z, then X bears the relation to Z.

Note that postulate (I) entails that each event belongs to exactly one world line.

> *Postulate II*   There are at least two mutually disjoint world lines.

The next two postulates concern causal connectibility, a notion we described explicitly in Section 3a, using Grünbaum's terms "*k*-connection" and "physically possible." (The only difference is a linguistic one: in our formulation, "causally connectible" is not a defined or complex predicate, but a simple predicate.)

> *Postulate III*   Causal connectibility is a binary reflexive and symmetric relation among events.

> *Postulate IV*   If two events are genidentical, then they are causally connectible.

Postulates (III) and (IV) are mainly concerned with making our usage of the terms explicit. The theory would not flounder if we decided to use "causal connectibility" to denote a relation disjoint from identity and genidentity; our present use would still be definable as the disjunction "causally connectible or identical or genidentical." But whichever usage is adopted, it needs to be made explicit.

> *Definition 2*   Two events are *topologically simultaneous* if and only if they are not causally connectible.

> *Definition 3*   Two events are *coincident* if and only if: any event is causally connectible with the one if and only if it is causally connectible with the other.

Note that coincidence does not entail genidentity; two bodies might, after all, touch each other. We may also note that, in our usage, coincidence does not imply topological simultaneity; this usage, however, is again primarily a matter of choice of linguistic convention.

We shall now introduce a convenient fiction: Every body exists, and has existed, as long as every other body (hence, "as long as time," or at least, as long as the world).

Postulate V If event E is not on world line W, then W contains events E' and E'' such that E and E' are topologically simultaneous and E and E'' are causally connectible.

To dispense with this idealization would make our theory more complicated, but not essentially so.

By the postulates and definitions above, the *class of events in W that are topologically simultaneous* with E is not empty exactly when E is an event not in the world line W. This is a very important kind of class; we shall call it a *simultaneity class* (of E on W).

Definition 4 The *simultaneity class of E on W*—in symbols, "Sim $W(E)$"—is the class of all events in W that are topologically simultaneous with E.

Postulate (V) then says that each world line is entirely covered by simultaneity classes. This postulate helps us to define a continuous part of a world line.

Definition 5 The class of *continuous parts* of a world line W is the smallest collection of parts of W such that the following holds:
(a) if E is not on W, Sim $W(E)$ is a continuous part of W;
(b) if X_1 and X_2 are continuous parts of W and overlap, then their common part is a continuous part of W;
(c) if X_1 and X_2 are continuous parts of W and overlap, then their sum is a continuous part of W.

The next postulate is motivated by the consideration that we conceive of world lines as not containing temporal gaps.

Postulate VI If E and E' are events in the world line W, then there is a continuous part P of W to which E and E' both belong (P "connects" E and E').

Now we can define temporal pair separation on a world line in the way this is done in Grünbaum's second formulation of the theory.

Definition 6 If events *E*, *X*, *E′*, and *Y* all belong to world line *W*, then *X* and *Y* *temporally separate E and E′*—in symbols, "*S(X,Y/E,E′)*"—*on W* if and only if every continuous part of *W* that connects *E* and *E′* contains either *X* or *Y*.

Here we must say something about the possibility that time is closed.[13] At first sight, any two events are causally connectible if time is closed, for it seems that we could send out a signal so slow that it goes all the way "around time" before it arrives at its destination. In this way we could have a light signal from *A* to *A′* and back (emission *E*, reflection *R*, absorption *F*) and a slow signal emitted from *A′* coincidently with *R*, but arriving locally between *E* and *F*.

We have two alternatives: we can admit that this is so or we can show why we can allow it to be ruled out (as is done by Postulate [V]). In the first case, the situation is rather like that for open time *without* the assumption that nothing can go faster than light. From a logical point of view, this problem is just as interesting, but we are not inclined to consider it, since contemporary physics does make this assumption. If we try to state this assumption in nonmetric terms, we arrive at a principle that does eliminate the difficulty raised in the preceding paragraph. The assumption that light provides a limiting velocity for signals will be stated first in terms of *before*, then in terms of *between*, then in terms of *pair separation*.

before If the emission of a light signal from *A* is coincident with the emission of some other signal from *A*, then the arrival of the light signal at *A′* is before the arrival of that other signal at *A′*.

between If a light signal travels from *A* to *A′* and back, and some other signal between *A* and *A′* has one terminus coincident with the reflection of this light signal, then its other terminus is not between the emission and absorption of the light signal.

pair separation If a light signal travels from *A* to *A′* and back, and other two signals have termini coincident with the reflection of this light signal, then their other termini do not separate the emission and absorption of the light signal.

The last formulation rules out the possibility of going all the way "around time" in such a way that one thing or signal would exist at two places at the same time or establish a signal connection "faster" than light.

It is now advantageous to begin to formulate our ideas in terms of coordinates. We shall leave open the possibilities that time is both open and closed. But we shall not admit such possibilities as that "time travel" exists or that time has the topological structure of a figure eight.

> *Definition 7* A function t is a (*topologically*) *admissible time-coordinate assignment* if and only if
> (a) t maps all events either onto the real-number system or onto the extended real-number system;
> (b) if E, X, E', and Y belong to the same world line W, then $t(X)$ and $t(Y)$ numerically separate $t(E)$ and $t(E')$ if and only if X and Y temporally separate E and E' on W;
> (c) if E and E' are coincident, then $t(E) = t(E')$;
> (d) if E and E' are not coincident, then $t(E) = t(E')$ only if E and E' are topologically simultaneous.

(To say that t maps all events *onto* the real numbers means that each real number is the coordinate of some event. We are clearly using the idealization (or assumption) of *point events*, events that "last no more than an instant.") Clauses (a)–(d) exhaust the conditions we can place on such coordinate assignments in accordance with the preceding discussion. But what if the facts are such that there are no admissible time-coordinate assignments in the sense of the definition above? This question necessitates a further postulate of adequacy. We shall use a strong postulate, which also has other important consequences.

> *Postulate VII Either* all admissible time-coordinate assignments map all events onto the real-number system *or* all admissible time-coordinate assignments map all events onto the extended real-number system, *but not both*.

The logically minded reader will note that this postulate entails that there is at least one admissible time-coordinate assignment in the sense defined (otherwise, both disjuncts would be true). Also, it entails that every world line is topologically open or topologically closed and does not have the topological structure of a figure eight: for example, if W is a figure eight, it is not the case that for all x, y, z, and w on W, either $S(x,y/z,w)$ or $S(x,w/z,y)$ or $S(x,z/w,y)$—but this is a property of numerical pair separation. Finally, this postulate rules out the deviant possibility of some world lines being open and some closed. (The last consequence may be viewed as part of our fiction that each world line lasts "as long as the world.")

5. Extension to a Theory of Space-Time

We turn in this section to the introduction of the time metric and spatial relations. This is a subject to which the philosopher has little to contribute beyond the clarification of the foundations of relativity theory recounted in Chapter V. What is needed is an exposition of how the transition can be made from the causal theory of time order to the theory of space-time implicit in the theory of relativity.

In the special theory of relativity, a certain class of physical systems have a special status: the inertial systems. When a clock is rigidly attached to an inertial system—or *is* an inertial system—we shall call it an *inertial clock*. What is a standard clock? In principle, one may choose as standard clocks any family of clocks that are mutually equivalent in Poincaré's sense. But this criterion may leave us with several candidates for this status.[14] The practice is to count as standard what are known as "mechanical clocks": simple harmonic oscillators.[15] In addition, we require them to be inertial clocks.

A standard clock measures space-time intervals along its own world line; if we take its position as the spatial origin of the frame of reference, it measures time intervals along its own world line. This is not so much a fact as a stipulation (in part) of the time metric we shall accept—as, of course, is done in the special theory of relativity.

To make this precise, let C be a standard clock, and X and Y

events on the world line of C. We shall use "$C(X)$," "$C(Y)$" to denote the readings of C coincident with X and Y, respectively. We can then state our stipulation as follows: t is an *assignment of time coordinates determined by* C only if $t(X) = C(X) + k$ for all events X on the world line of C, for some constant k.

If Z is an event not on the world line of C, what conditions should we place on $t(Z)$ in this case? We shall use the Einstein convention discussed in Chapter V. If W is the world line of C, we consider the class of numbers $t(X)$ for the events X belonging to $\text{Sim}\,W(Z)$. These form an open interval (t_1, t_2) of real numbers. We now stipulate

$$t(Z) = t_1 + \frac{t_2 - t_1}{2}$$

where $t_1 < t_2$ (that is just how we chose the names "t_1" and "t_2").

Now we define a *metrically admissible assignment of time coordinates* to be a topologically admissible such assignment that is determined by some standard clock C. This finishes the job of introducing a time metric. But a metrically admissible assignment of time coordinates still represents only part of an inertial frame of reference. In such a frame, every event has spatial coordinates as well as a time coordinate.

Spatial relations obtain between events that happen at the same time. The special theory of relativity postulates that these relations, among all the events at a given time, are correctly described by Euclidean geometry. Second, Euclidean geometry can be axiomatized using the notion of *distance* as only primitive term (see Chapter IV, Section 2d). So now we must simply define the distance between two events happening at the same time; this last qualification means: two events that are assigned the same time coordinate. Well, if they both belong to the same world line, the distance between them is zero. If they do not belong to the same world line, we shall define the distance between them (as in Chapter V) by saying that in an inertial frame the velocity of light is arbitrarily set equal to one.

To state this precisely, we shall now describe the conditions under which an assignment F of temporal and spatial coordinates will be called a *frame of reference* (determined by a given clock C).

First, let t be the metrically admissible assignment of time coordinates determined by C. Then the time coordinate of an event X in F is $t(X)$. Second, every event on the world line W of C has spatial coordinates $(0,0,0)$. Third, if X and Y have spatial coordinates (x,y,z) and (x',y',z'), the spatial distance in F between them is $\sqrt{(x-x')^2 + (y-y')^2 + (z-z')^2}$, and we must place further conditions on that magnitude.

First, if Y but not X is on the world line of C, then $(x',y',z') = (0,0,0)$ and the distance between Y and X in F, that is, $\sqrt{x^2 + y^2 + z^2}$, must equal $(1/2)|t_2 - t_1|$, where the time coordinates of the events in $\mathrm{Sim}W(X)$ form the interval (t_1, t_2).

Now let W' be a world line of a standard clock whose distance from W is constant and let X but not Y lie on W'. Then the distance between X and Y in F is $(1/2)|t_2 - t_1|$ where the time coordinates of the events in $\mathrm{Sim}W'(Y)$ form the interval (t_1, t_2). We have not defined all distances yet, since not every place is the locus of a standard clock. But the most we can do is to require the spatial metric to satisfy this condition. (This is all that can be meant by the frequent idealization of supposing every place to have a clock attached to it.)

To complete our job we should now postulate that this condition allows the distances to satisfy the relevant postulates for Euclidean geometry, and then stipulate that F is an *inertial frame of reference* if, in addition, these postulates *are* satisfied.

It is easy to see that the choice of a family of standard clocks amounts, at the same time, to the choice of a "direction of time": any two such clocks "run in the same direction," because otherwise they could not be equivalent in the sense of Poincaré. We must add the duration postulate, and we must also postulate that each standard clock has in each frame of reference a constant velocity. This entails that points on the world line of an inertial clock lie on the same straight line in any frame. The importance of this is that if C' is an inertial clock not at rest in F, a Euclidean transformation of the spatial coordinates in F suffices to make the X-axis of F coincide with the line of motion of C'. This is a necessary preamble to the deduction of the Lorentz transformations in the way this was done in Chapter V, Section 5. The deduction there pertains to a simple case. But we can always obtain this simple case by a Euclidean transformation of the spatial coordinates and a displacement of the temporal coordinates ("resetting the clock"). For the sake of brevity, we shall call this whole transformation Euclidean.

We must be very clear about exactly what is established in this way and what we intend to accept as convention. First, if two frames are determined by clocks C and C', such that C' is at rest in the frame determined by C, then a simple calculation from the duration postulate shows that the coordinates of actual events in the frame determined by C' result from those they have in the frame determined by C by means of a Euclidean transformation. Second, suppose that C' is in motion in the frame of C. Then the calculations in Chapter V, Section 5, show that the coordinates of actual events in the frame determined by C' result from the coordinates these events have in the frame determined by C by means of Euclidean and Lorentz transformations.

These results we take as our reason to define an admissible frame of reference to be one that is determined by a standard (inertial) clock or to result from such a frame by means of Euclidean and/or Lorentz transformations. This is, in part, conventional, because not every place is equipped with a standard clock. But the objective factual presupposition—that coordinates of actual events in frames determined by standard clocks are thus related—has been shown to be satisfied.

We are now justified in claiming that the causal theory of time provides a foundation of the special theory of relativity, in the sense that it can be axiomatically extended into a complete theory of the space-time of special relativity.[16]

6. The Role of Idealization and Modal Concepts

a. Pointlike Particles and Events

When we say that the position of a body or event in space is represented by a triple (x,y,z) of real numbers, or in time by a single real number t, we are obviously idealizing. For any actual body has a certain finite volume, so that its location is not a point but a three-dimensional region in space. Similarly, common examples of states and events last a certain finite amount of time; their location in time is properly represented by a finite interval on the real line.

What, then, is the relevance of a theory treating of *pointlike* bodies (particles) and events? (The same question may be asked, of course, for particle mechanics and geometrical optics.) The answer has two parts; both are variations on the theme that we deal with a *model* of the subject we study and that this is a proper method of inquiry.

The first part of the answer is that a problem about, say, the motion of actual bodies may be *approximated* by an analogous problem about point particles. For example, the motions of moon and earth can be roughly approximated by a model of two point particles m_1 and m_2, such that m_1 has the same mass as the moon and is located at the moon's center and m_2 similarly represents the earth.

The second part of the answer is that a problem about, say, the motion of an actual body may be treated quite precisely (without approximation) by *regarding* the body as an infinite system of point particles of constant configuration, occupying the same volume as that body. The laws governing such a system are deducible from the laws governing the individual particles, and the relations among these particles.

In other words, the idealization involved in limiting our attention to point particles in mechanics is but a method used to arrive at (what we assert to be) an adequate model for the behavior of actual bodies—and, *mutatis mutandis*, for events.

Too much hinges on the relation between model and actuality in this answer for it to satisfy the philosopher as it stands. It needs an underpinning in the form of a thorough discussion of the relation in question and of the use and role of models. In this context the important point concerning these misgivings, however, is that they concern a general problem in no way peculiar to the philosophy of time and space. In this respect, we can feel quite sanguine about our use of these idealizations.

Could we have developed the theory of time, say, on the premise that all events have finite duration? An admissible coordinate assignment would then have to assign a finite interval of coordinates to events. Whitehead and Russell did approach the matter in this way. But they postulated that every finite part of an event is itself an event and that any sum of events that touch each other is an event, as well as various other facts about the cardinality and distribution of events.[17] In my opinion, these postulates are no more plausible than the postulate that every event is made up of pointlike events. (The latter postulate would at once solve the problem of how the point-event model is related to actual events.) Under these circumstances, I prefer to use the punctal model and leave open its relation to actual events.[18]

b. Axiomatization and Explication

In our final version of the causal theory of time, the only primitive concept added to the framework of objects and events is *causal connectibility*. According to our theory, this relation is equivalent to a certain spatiotemporal relation among events, in the sense that the following is a theorem:

(9) X is causally connectible with Y if and only if X and Y are either spatiotemporally coincident or temporally separated.*

Because of this, we have to defend ourselves against the charge that the causal theory of time and space is trivial, because it has simply given a new name ("causally connectible") to the spatiotemporal relation described in (9).

What does this criticism entail? If it is correct, we may have succeeded in developing a *relational* theory of space-time, but not a *causal* theory thereof. For we have not postulated the existence of absolute time or of instants—but the causal theory goes beyond the relational theory precisely in the claim that all spatiotemporal relations can be defined in terms of physical relations. And whatever physical relations may be, they are not specifically temporal or spatial.

Now, "X and Y are causally connectible" means "It is

---

* We chose causal connectibility rather than topological simultaneity to contain the relation of coincidence; this is obviously not essential, but it is a convenient convention.

physically possible that X and Y are causally connected." We shall therefore have to consider both the notion of physical possibility and the notion of causal connection. The former we shall postpone until Section 6c; the latter we shall consider now.

Given the devastating criticism that notions of causality have suffered at the hands of modern philosophers, the argument that "causally connected" expresses a physical relation may not seem an easy task to prove. And we should certainly be in a predicament if we had to provide a general account of the notion of physical relation in the course of such an argument. But I think the situation is rather less precarious. For in the causal theory of space-time, the term "causally connected" has a very restricted use. Its use does not involve any general notion of causality; "X is causally connected with Y" is used as equivalent to "Either X and Y belong to the history of one and the same object, or belong to the history of one and the same signal, or are coincident with some pair of events thus connected." Genidentity and signal connection are relations too basic in the conceptual scheme of physics and too empirical in their significance to be denied the status of physical relations, it seems to me, even in the absence of necessary and sufficient criteria for the applicability of the term "physical relation." From this we draw the following conclusion: "causally connected," and hence "causally connectible," have a meaning that is not specifically spatiotemporal. Therefore, we are not guilty of the sleight of hand of developing a causal theory of time by giving a new name to a basic spatiotemporal relation.

But we must face another criticism: "causally connected" does not mean simply "genidentical or signal connected"; it also applies to pairs of events that are spatiotemporally coincident with another pair of events thus connected. Hence, part of the meaning of "causally connectible" is purely spatiotemporal. This we counter by saying that the equivalences in question hold within the context of our theory, in which "coincident" is defined in terms of causal connectibility. But one may hear the criticism: However you define your notions, the meaning of "causal connectibility" cannot be given without the use of spatiotemporal terms.

This is a very old kind of argument; it is essentially Kant's argument against Leibniz, which we discussed in Chapter II, Sections 3b and 3c(i). Our position here is that within natural language there is no defining-defined hierarchy and that there is no such thing as "the" meaning of a term, although there are meaning relations (inclusion, equivalence) among terms. Within a specific formulation, some terms are defined and others undefined, but the status of being defined is not invariant under transitions to other formulations of the same theory. The claim of the causal theory of time is not that spatiotemporal terms are *defined*, but that they are *definable*, in terms of causal connectibility. (And causal connectibility is definable in terms of spatiotemporal coincidence, plus some other notions; this no one denies.) Formulations of theories are, in a sense, artificial, since they must rely on a choice of primitive terms (and of axioms) that is to some extent arbitrary. But a dictionary (say, of English) is circular and should be, for in natural languages there are no inherent definitional hierarchies.

What, then, is the status of (9)? It is an equivalence following from the definitions in our theory, but it is more than that. No matter how we choose our definitions, (9) should follow as a theorem (with the qualification given in the footnote)—that is, we accept (9) as one of the *criteria* of *adequacy* for *any* formulation of the theory. Our adherence to (9) is a linguistic commitment, based on our acceptance of the basic theses of the causal theory of space-time, transcending the adherence to any particular version of this theory.

c. Causal Connectibility and Space-Time

The term "causally connectible" is called a *modal* term because it expresses a possibility (of actual connection). "Causally connected" is the corresponding nonmodal term. The reason for using the modal term is simple: the seemingly insuperable difficulties involved in making do with nonmodal terms. The most important point here is that it is purely contingent whether there are any actual signal and genidentity connections in any given part of the universe. One might postulate that there are enough such connections to define temporal order for all events (given, one must assume, some other relations). And this postulate might be made plausible by accepted physical theory. In a philosophical account, however, one prefers to make as few empirical assumptions as possible.[19]

But the meaning of modal terms itself needs philosophical explication; this is generally agreed. If we take "*X* and *Y* are causally connectible" to be equivalent to "It is physically possible for *X* and *Y* to be causally connected," we must face the demand for an explication of *physical possibility*. But here we are in a quandary. For the attempted accounts of physical possibility are along the following line: Something is physically possible exactly if it is not ruled out by physical laws. The only way, however, in which physical laws can rule out that the emission and absorption of some signal should coincide with *X* and *Y*, respectively, is on the basis of the relative spatiotemporal positions of *X* and *Y*—or so it would seem.

What we really have here is a counterfactual conditional:

X is causally connectible with *Y* if and only if a signal emitted coincidently with *X* *would* arrive coincidently with *Y*, or conversely.

In other words, we have again arrived at a general problem (the problem of counterfactuals) transcending the problems of space and time proper. But on this problem some philosophers have taken the stand that in philosophical accounts one should eschew modal qualifiers and counterfactual connectives ("possibly," "if . . . were the case") altogether. In using "connectible" are we not courting the danger of violating philosophical standards of clarity?

To answer we may first point out that there are many philosophers who hold that common modal discourse is as intelligible as any (without thereby denying the desirability of an account, of course). Second, we may refer to the writings of a major critic of modal discourse, W. V. O. Quine, to show that we are certainly not violating his standards. Quine demands that the language of science or philosophy contain only the standard logical and mathematical words, plus a set of nonlogical predicates (corresponding to the English form of "is" followed by an adjective or "is a" followed by a noun), and *no* modal qualifiers, counterfactual "if . . . then"s, and so on. For our purpose, however, the crucial passage is the following:

> From recent paragraphs it becomes evident not only that the subjunctive [i.e. counterfactual] conditional has no place in an austere canonical notation for science, but also that the ban on it is less restrictive than would at first appear. We remain free to allow ourselves one by one any general terms we like, however subjunctive or dispositional their explanations.[20]

In other words, Quine's demand for austerity does not rule out our use of "connectible," provided only that we do not use its longer equivalent "possibly connected" (except in informal commentary). In this we are able, and happy, to oblige him. I suspect Quine was driven to this concession by the impossibility of drawing a distinction between terms that are truly modal and terms equivalent in meaning to some modal construction. One less committed to austerity, or more impressed by the resources of natural language, might have abandoned all opposition to the use of modal constructions at this point (though not the hope for their explication, of course).

It seems, therefore, that, as presently formulated, the causal theory of time meets the standards of clarity currently imposed. But after having said this, I would like to argue that we can look upon our use of the counterfactual notion of connectibility as a dispensable convenience rather than as a necessity. In view of the difficulties that have been pointed out, this position is perhaps somewhat audacious, and the reader will recognize that the status of the causal theory of time does not hinge on the success of my argument here.

To put it baldly, the structure of actual physical connections does not determine, as far as we can see, the spatiotemporal relations among actual events—as these are usually conceived. So we use a relation of connectibility to define these relations, after having laid down suitable postulates on the relational structure of connectibility. But these postulates are calculated to make the structure of temporal relations, as defined, isomorphic to the (extended) real-number system, for example. My proposal is therefore that we look upon the use of the connectibility relation as simply having the purpose of describing the logical space in which, we assert, all relational structures of actual connections can be embedded. This means that we think that the relation of connectibility is not needed to describe the actual world. It means also that the postulates on connectibility that we lay down just express a belief concerning the actual connections we may encounter, and nothing more.

If this position is accepted, it follows that our construction of the theory of time and space has been calculated to provide intuitive content for its notions rather than to provide a concise theoretical development. For on the present position, the causal theory of time may be summed up as follows: Whatever actual physical connections there are must be reflected in the logical space; a certain mathematical structure is such that whatever actual physical connections there are can be reflected in it in this manner; and we choose this mathematical structure as the logical space *time*. The postulates on connectibility only helped to single out the mathematical structure in question in a heuristic manner.

This position is attractive to me because it is a "conceptualist" rather than a "realist" position on the subject of the truth of counterfactual assertions, at least as they appear in the theory of time and space.[21] It is also in greater harmony with the conception of time as a logical space, it seems to me, though the "realist" position can also accommodate this conception. But I also think that the position is not worthwhile on its own, that is, unless it can be extended into a tenable theory of counterfactuals in general.

Notes

Chapter I Basic Issues in the Philosophy of Time and Space

1. Cf. W. V. O. Quine, "On What There Is," *From a Logical Point of View* (New York: Harper & Row, 1963), pp. 1–19.

Chapter II The Problems of the Theory of Time:
Aristotle to Kant

1. Bk. IV, secs. 10–14, in *Aristotle's Physics,* 217b, 30—244a, 20, R. Hope, tr. (Lincoln: University of Nebraska Press, 1961).
2. *Ibid.,* Bk. V, sec. 1; cf. *Aristotle's Metaphysics,* J. Warrington, tr. (New York: Dutton, 1956), Bk. IX, secs. 9, 11, 12.
3. *Physics, op. cit.,* Bk. V, 224b, 28–29.
4. *Ibid.,* 225a, 3–5, 15–17.
5. *Ibid.,* 219a, 13–22.
6. St. Thomas Aquinas, *Commentary on Aristotle's "Physics,"* R. J.

Blackwell *et al.,* trs. (New Haven: Yale University Press, 1963), Bk. IV, 17, sec. 577.

7. *Physics, op. cit.,* Bk. VIII, 261b, 25 ff.

8. See also *ibid.,* Bk. IV, 223b, 15–224a, 2.

9. *Ibid.,* 218a, 30 ff.

10. *Ibid.,* 218b, 14–15.

11. *Ibid.,* 218b, 21 ff.

12. *Ibid.,* 219a, 1–3.

13. *Ibid.,* 219a, 10–35.

14. *Ibid.,* 219b, 1–5.

15. *Ibid.,* 219b, 1–10.

16. *Ibid.,* 223b, 1–5.

17. *Ibid.,* 223b, 5–10; 224a, 2–19.

18. *Ibid.,* 251b, 10–15, 18–28.

19. *Ibid.,* 218b, 21–30.

20. Aquinas, *op. cit.,* Bk. VIII, 2, sec. 990; St. Thomas Aquinas, *Commentary on the Metaphysics of Aristotle,* J. P. Rowan, tr. (Chicago: Regnery, 1961), Bk. XII, 5, sec. 2498.

21. *The Geometrical Lectures of Isaac Barrow,* J. M. Child, tr. (La Salle, Ill.: Open Court, 1916), pp. 35–37.

22. Cf. E. A. Burtt, *The Metaphysical Foundations of Modern Science* (New York: Anchor Books, 1932), Chap. V, sec. F.

23. F. Cajori, ed., *Sir Isaac Newton's Mathematical Principles of Natural Philosophy and His System of the World* (Berkeley: University of California Press, 1960), pp. 6, 8.

24. Cf. Burtt, *op. cit.,* Chap. VII, sec. 4C.

25. H. G. Alexander, ed., *The Leibniz-Clarke Correspondence* (Manchester, Eng.: Manchester University Press, 1956).

26. *Ibid.,* Clarke, Fourth Reply, sec. 15.

27. *Ibid.,* Leibniz, Fifth Letter, secs. 55–57.

28. *Ibid.,* Clarke, Fifth Reply, sec. 55.

29. J. Locke, *An Essay Concerning Human Understanding,* A. C. Fraser, ed. (New York: Dover, 1959), Bk. II, xiv, 24.

30. *Ibid.,* II, xiv, 30.

31. G. Leibniz, *New Essays Concerning Human Understanding,* A. G. Langley, tr. (La Salle, Ill.: Open Court, 1916), Bk. II, sec. xiv, 24.

32. *Ibid.,* II, xv, 11.

33. Cf. N. Goodman, *Fact, Fiction, and Forecast* (Cambridge, Mass.: Harvard University Press, 1955), Chaps. I–II.

34. F. Cajori, ed., *Sir Isaac Newton's Mathematical Principles of Natural Philosophy and His System of the World* (Berkeley, University of California Press, 1960).

35. *Physics, op. cit.,* 221b, 20–222a, 9.

36. Cf. B. C. van Fraassen, "Foundations of the Causal Theory of Time," unpublished Ph.D. dissertation, University of Pittsburgh, 1966, Chap. II.

37. P. Bridgman, *A Sophisticate's Primer of Relativity* (New York: Harper & Row, 1965), p. 115.

38. G. H. von Wright, *Norm and Action* (London: Routledge and Kegan Paul, 1963), p. 27; B. Russell, *The Principles of Mathematics* (London: Allen and Unwin, 1956), pp. 469–473.

39. Van Fraassen, *op. cit.,* Chap. II, sec. B.

40. H. Reichenbach, *Elements of Symbolic Logic* (New York: Macmillan, 1947), sec. 48; H. Reichenbach, *The Direction of Time* (Berkeley: University of California Press, 1956), sec. 26.

41. Cf. van Fraassen, *op. cit.,* Chap. II, secs. B4, D.

42. H. G. Alexander, *op. cit.,* Clarke, Third Reply, sec. 4.

43. Cf. H. Reichenbach, "The Theory of Motion According to Newton, Leibniz, and Huygens," *Modern Philosophy of Science* (London: Routledge and Kegan Paul, 1959), pp. 46–66.

44. I. M. Bochenski, *A History of Formal Logic* (Notre Dame, Ind.: University of Notre Dame Press, 1961). 12–23.

45. N. K. Smith (ed.), *Kant's Inaugural Dissertation and Early Writings on Space,* J. Handyside, tr. (La Salle, Ill.: Open Court, 1929), p. 58.

46. P. P. Wiener, ed., *Leibniz: Selections* (New York: Scribner, 1951), pp. 201–202.

47. *Ibid.*

48. Alexander, *op. cit.,* p. 38.

49. Wiener, *op. cit.,* pp. 201–202.

50. Cf. C. G. Hempel, *Aspects of Scientific Explanation* (New York: Free Press, 1965), pp. 421–423.

51. For a more complete account see I. M. Bochenski, *Contemporary European Philosophy* (Berkeley: University of California Press, 1956), and I. M. Bochenski, *Methods of Contemporary Thought* (Dordrecht, Holland: Reidel, 1965).

52. E. Husserl, *Cartesian Meditations* (The Hague: Nijhoff, 1960), sec. 34.

53. R. Carnap, *Meaning and Necessity,* 2nd ed. (Chicago: University of Chicago Press, 1956), Appendix D.

54. D. Hume, *A Treatise of Human Nature,* ed. L. A. Selby-Bigge (Oxford: The Clarendon Press, 1896), Bk. I, Pt. II.

55. For Kant's own remarks on his philosophical method, see I. Kant, *Critique of Pure Reason,* N. K. Smith, tr. (New York: St. Martin's Press, 1956), B263–B264.

56. Cf. P. F. Strawson, *The Bounds of Sense* (London: Methuen, 1966), pp. 125–139, and also G. Martin, *Kant's Metaphysics and Theory of Science* (Manchester, Eng.: Manchester University Press, 1961), Chap. III.

57. Kant, *Critique.*, B219.

58. *Ibid.,* A188.

59. *Ibid.,* B234.

60. *Ibid.,* A211.

61. *Ibid.,* B256.

62. *Ibid.,* B260.

63. *Ibid.,* B257.

64. *Ibid.,* A218.

65. See *Ibid.,* A214–A215.

66. *Ibid.,* A218.

67. In the discussion which follows I have relied on H. Mehlberg, "Essai sur la théorie causale du temps," *Studia Philosophica,* I (1935), 119–260; II (1937), 111–231.

68. Mehlberg, *op. cit.,* Pt. I, p. 160 (citation from Lechalas, my translation).

69. *Ibid.,* p. 164.

70. *Ibid.*

71. "... au moment où celui-là se trouve dans l'état. ..."

Chapter III   The Problems of the Theory of Time: the Nineteenth Century

1. Cf. F. Nietzsche, *The Will to Power,* W. Kaufmann and R. J. Hollingdale, trs. (New York: Random House, 1967), Bk. IV, Chap. III,; also A. Danto, *Nietzsche as Philosopher* (New York: Macmillan, 1965), pp. 205–209.

2. Cf. A. Rey, *Le Retour éternel et la philosophie de la physique* (Paris: Flammarion, 1927).

3. H. Bois, "Le Retour éternel de Nietzsche," *L'Anneé Philosophique*, 24 (1913), 145–184; citation from pp. 172–173 (my translation).

4. See also M. Capek, "The Theory of Eternal Recurrence in Modern Philosophy of Science, With Special Reference to C. S. Peirce," *Journal of Philosophy*, 57 (April 28, 1960), 289–296; and B. C. van Fraassen, "Capek on Eternal Recurrence," *Journal of Philosophy*, 59 (July 5, 1962), 371–375.

5. Cf. M. Black, "The Identity of Indiscernibles," *Mind*, New Series 51 (April 1952), 153–164.

6. Cf. van Fraassen, *op. cit.*, sec. IV; A. Grünbaum, *Philosophical Problems of Space and Time* (New York: Knopf, 1963), pp. 197–203.

7. C. Hartshorne and P. Weiss, eds., *Collected Papers of Charles Sanders Peirce* (Cambridge, Mass.: Harvard University Press, 1960), I, 274, 498; VI, 210; VIII, 317. See also fn. 4.

8. Cf. B. E. Meserve, *Fundamental Concepts of Geometry* (Reading, Mass.: Addison-Wesley, 1955), Chap. 3, sec. 7.

9. Alexander, *op. cit.*, Clarke, Third Reply, par. 4, p. 32.

10. *Ibid.*, Leibniz, Fifth Letter, par. 54, p. 75.

11. *Ibid.*, par. 105, pp. 89–90.

12. *Ibid.*, Clarke, Fifth Reply, par. 54, p. 105.

13. Wiener, *op. cit.*, pp. 202–203.

14. *Ibid.*, p. 205.

15. Cf. Alexander, *op. cit.*, pp. xliv–xlv.

16. L. Euler, *Opera Omnia*, F. Rudo *et al.*, eds., Series III (Berlin: Teubner, 1911–1967), Vol. II, pp. 376–383. Cf. Alexander, *op. cit.*, pp. xliii–xliv, and W. H. Werkmeister, *A Philosophy of Science* (New York: Harper & Row, 1940), pp. 61–63.

17. H. Poincaré, *The Value of Science*, Chap. II, sec. III; reprinted in H. Poincaré, *The Foundations of Science* (New York: Science Press, 1913), pp. 201–358.

18. *Ibid.*, Chap. II, sec. V.

19. Grünbaum, *op. cit.*, pp. 139, 144–146.

20. Poincaré, *op. cit.*, Chap. II, sec IV.

21. B. Russell, *An Essay on the Foundations of Geometry* (Cambridge, Eng.: Cambridge University Press, 1897); the exchange with Poincaré can be found in the *Revue de métaphysique et de morale*, 7 (May 1899), 251–279, 7 (Nov. 1899) 684–707; 8 (Jan. 1900), 73–86.

22. B. Bosanquet, *Logic* (Oxford: Clarendon, 1888), pp. 178–180.

23. Russell, *Essay, op. cit.,* sec. 151, pp. 156–157.

24. A. N. Whitehead, *Essays in Science and Philosophy* (New York: Philosophical Library, 1947), p. 265.

25. B. Russell, *My Philosophical Development* (London: Allen and Unwin, 1959), p. 62.

26. *Ibid.,* pp. 62–64. Whitehead's position and the naive realist position taken by Russell circa 1900 are discussed by Grünbaum, *op. cit.,* pp. 44–48, 48–65.

27. Cf. R. Taylor, "Moving About in Time," *Philosophical Quarterly,* 9 (Oct. 1959), pp. 289–301; B. Mayo, "Objects, Events and Complementarity," *Philosophical Review,* 70 (July 1961), pp. 340–361; F. I. Dretske, "Moving Backward in Time," *Philosophical Review,* 71 (Jan. 1962), pp. 94–98.

28. Cf. Grünbaum, *op. cit.,* pp. 240–242.

29. L. Boltzmann, *Lectures on Gas Theory,* S. G. Brush, tr. (Berkeley: University of California Press, 1964), pp. 446–447.

30. Reichenbach, *Direction of Time, op. cit.,* secs. 14–16; Grünbaum, *op. cit.,* Chap. 8., pp. 254–263, and "The anisotropy of time," in T. Gold and D. L. Schumacher, eds., *The Nature of Time* (Ithaca, N. Y.: Cornell University Press, 1967), pp. 149–174; O. Costa de Beauregard, *Le Second Principe de la science du temps* (Paris: Editions du Seuil, 1963).

31. Grünbaum, *Philosopical Problems of Space and Time, op. cit.,* pp. 264–280.

32. Boltzmann, *op. cit.,* p. 446.

33. *Physics, op. cit.,* 223a, 21–29; quoted from W. D. Ross, ed., *Aristotle's Physics* (Oxford: Clarendon, 1936).

34. *Commentary on Aristotle's "Physics", op. cit.,* lec. 17, 572–574.

35. *Ibid.,* lec. 23, 629.

36. B. Landry, *La Philosophie de Duns Scot* (Paris: Firmin-Didot, 1922), pp. 126–127.

37. R. Descartes, *The Principles of Philosophy,* in J. Veitch, tr., *The Meditations and Selections from the Principles of René Descartes* (La Salle, Ill.: Open Court, 1901), secs. I, LV, LVIII; B. de Spinoza, "Thoughts on Metaphysics," printed as Appendix to his *The Principles of the Philosophy of Descartes,* H. H. Britan, tr. (Chicago: Open Court, 1905), secs. I, IV.

38. Wiener, *op. cit.,* pp. 231, 247, 253, 272–273.

39. Euler, "Réflexions sur l'espace et le temps," *Opera Omnia, op. cit.,* II, 376–383.

40. Leibniz, *op. cit., New Essays,*II, XIV, secs. 24, 26.

41. Smith, ed., *op. cit.* (see note 45 of ch. II), p. 40.

42. L. Wittgenstein, *Tractatus Logico-Philosophicus,* D. F. Pears and B. F. McGuinness, trs. (London: Routledge and Kegan Paul, 1961), pp. 9, 11, 13, 15.

43. Kant, *Critique of Pure Reason, op. cit.,* A31.

44. *Ibid.,* A33.

45. For further discussion of the role and nature of logical spaces, see B. C. van Fraassen, "Meaning Relations Among Predicates," *Nous,* 1 (May, 1967), 161–179.

46. P. Natorp, *Die logischen Grundlagen der exakten Wissenschaften* (Leipzig: Teubner, 1910), pp. 281–282 (my translation).

47. B. Russell, *Our Knowledge of the External World* (New York: Norton, 1929), pp. 123–128.

48. *Ibid.,* p. 128.

49. This is a case of what Sellars calls "extra-conceptual possibility"; cf. W. Sellars, *Science, Perception, and Reality* (New York: Humanities Press, 1963), p. 319.

50. Cf. G. H. Mead, "A Behavioristic Account of the Significant Symbol," *Journal of Philosophy,* XIX (Mar. 16, 1922), 157–163.

Chapter IV   The Classical Problems of the Theory of Space

1. F. Cajori, ed., *Sir Isaac Newton's Mathematical Principles of Natural Philosophy and His System of the World* (Berkeley: University of California Press, 1960), p. 6.

2. J. Keill, *An Introduction to Natural Philosophy* (London: Andrew Millar, 1758), p. 15.

3. Cajori, *op. cit.,* p. 8.

4. H. G. Alexander, ed., *The Leibniz-Clarke Correspondence* (Manchester, Eng.: Manchester University Press, 1956), p. 69.

5. *Ibid.,* pp. 70–71.

6. Cajori, *op. cit.,* p. 12.

7. Alexander, *op. cit.,* Leibniz, Fifth Letter, par. 53, p. 74.

8. Cajori, *op cit.,* p. 12.

9. This seems to be supported by paragraph 52 of Leibniz's fifth letter to Clarke; see Alexander, *op. cit.,* pp. 73–74.

10. D. M. Armstrong, ed., *Berkeley's Philosophical Writings* (New York: Collier Books, 1965), p. 268.

11. Cf. H. Reichenbach, "The Theory of Motion According to Newton, Leibniz, and Huygens," *Modern Philosophy of Science* (London: Routledge and Kegan Paul, 1959), and H. Reichenbach, *The Philosophy of Space and Time* (New York: Dover, 1958), pp. 213–218.

12. L. Euler, *Opera Omnia,* F. Rudo *et al.,* eds, Series III (Berlin: Teubner, 1911–1967), Vol. II, pp. 376–383.

13. Cajori, *op. cit.,* p. 8.

14. *Ibid.,* Corollary V, p. 20.

15. M. Jammer, *Concepts of Space* (New York: Harper & Row, 1960), pp. 138–139.

16. Quoted and discussed by Alexander, *op. cit.,* p. xliii.

17. G. Saccheri, *Euclides Vindicatus,* G. B. Halsted, tr. (Chicago: Open Court, 1920), Proposition XXXIII, p. 173.

18. H. Poincaré, *Science and Hypothesis,* Chap. III; reprinted in H. Poincaré, *The Foundations of Science* (New York: Science Press, 1913); cf. L. M. Blumenthal, *A Modern View of Geometry* (San Francisco: Freeman, 1961), pp. 177–179.

19. Cf. Blumenthal, *op. cit.,* Chap. VIII, secs. 4, 6.

20. Cf. B. E. Meserve, *Fundamental Concepts of Geometry* (Reading, Mass.: Addison–Wesley, 1955), p. 271.

21. Blumenthal, *op. cit.,* p. 55.

22. B. Riemann, "On the Hypotheses Which Lie at the Foundations of Geometry," H. S. White, tr., in D. E. Smith, ed., *A Source Book in Mathematics* (New York: McGraw–Hill, 1929), pp. 411–425.

23. Cf. Chap. III, sec. 2a and A Grünbaum, *Philosophical Problems of space and Time* (New York: Knopf, 1963), Chap. I; see also papers by C. Massey, B. van Fraassen, and A. Grünbaum in *Philosophy of Science* 36–37 (1969–1970), in press.

24. Blumenthal, *op. cit.,* Chaps. VII–VIII.

25. H. von Helmholtz, "Ueber die Thatsachen, die der Geometrie zugrunde liegen" (1868); reprinted in his *Schriften zur Erkenntnistheorie* (Berlin: Springer, 1921). An exposition may be found in H. von Helmholtz, *Popular Lectures on Scientific Subjects,* E. Atkinson, tr. (New York: Appleton, 1881), Chap. II, and in B. Russell, *An Essay on the Foundations of Geometry* (Cambridge, Eng.: Cambridge University Press, 1897), secs. 24–26.

26. Cf. Russell, *ibid.,* sec. 45, and A. N. Whitehead, *The Axioms of Descriptive Geometry* (Cambridge, Eng.: Cambridge University Press, 1907), Chap. V.

27. H. Poincaré, *op. cit.,* Chap. V, p. 81.

28. Helmholtz, *Popular Lectures, op. cit.,* Chap. II.

29. *Ibid.,* p. 58.

30. Reichenbach, *Philosophy of Space and Time, op. cit.,* secs. 3, 6.

31. Grünbaum, *op. cit.,* Chap. 3, sec. A.

32. Reichenbach, *Philosophy of Space and Time, op. cit.,* sec. 4.

33. Jammer, *op. cit.,* p. 172; G. J. Whitrow, "Why Physical Space Has Three Dimensions," *British Journal for the Philosophy of Science,* 6 (May 1955), 13–31.

34. G. Leibniz, *Theodicy,* E. M. Huggard, tr. (London: Routledge and Kegan Paul, 1951), sec. 351.

35. Cf. W. Hurewicz and H. Wallman, *Dimensions Theory* (Princeton, N.J.: Princeton University Press, 1941), p. 5.

36. Poincaré, *op. cit.,* pp. 52–53.

37. Cf. Hurewicz and Wallman, *op. cit.,* p. 4. Actually, Brouwer used the notion of connectedness, which is wider than that of continuity. See also G. Bouligand, *Les Définitions modernes de la dimension* (Paris: Hermann et Cie, 1935).

38. N. K. Smith, ed., *Kant's Inaugural Dissertation and Early Writings on Space,* J. Handyside, tr. (La Salle, Ill.: Open Court, 1929), pp. 10–12.

39. Cf. Jammer, *op. cit.,* p. 177.

40. Whitrow, *op. cit.;* see also the appendix to his *The Structure and Evolution of the Universe* (New York: Harper & Row, 1959) and Reichenbach, *Philosophy of Space and Time, op. cit.,* p. 280.

41. Grünbaum, *Philosophy of Space and Time, op. cit.,* pp. 332–333.

42. Russell, *An Essay on the Foundations of Geometry, op. cit.,* sec. 161.

43. N. K. Smith, ed., *op. cit.,* p. 26.

44. Grünbaum, *op. cit.,* pp. 330–332.

45. Reichenbach, *Philosophy of Space and Time, op. cit.,* secs. 12, 14.

46. *Ibid.,* p. 279.

Chapter V The Impact of the Theory of Relativity

1. Cf., e.g., R. D. Carmichael, *The Theory of Relativity* (New York: Wiley, 1913), pp. 10–13; D. Bohm, *The Special Theory of Relativity*

(New York: W. A. Benjamin, 1965), Chap. IV. Einstein's original paper can be found in H. A. Lorentz *et al., The Principle of Relativity, A Collection of Original Memoirs* (New York: Dover, 1952).

2. Cf. Bohm, *op. cit.*, Chap. V.

3. *Ibid.*, Chap. VI.

4. *Ibid.*, Chap. VII.

5. *Ibid.*, pp. 12–13, 29–30.

6. Cf. H. Reichenbach, *The Philosophy of Space and Time* (New York: Dover, 1958), sec. 19, and A. Grünbaum, *Philosophical Problems of Space and Time* (New York: Knopf, 1963), Chap. 12, sec. B.

7. Cf. B. Ellis and P. Bowman, "Conventionality in Distant Simultaneity," *Philosophy of Science* 34 (June 1967), 116–136, and the rejoinder by Grünbaum *et al., Philosophy of Science* 36 (March 1969), pp. 1–81.

8. Cf. Grünbaum, *Philosophical Problems of Space and Time, op. cit.*, pp. 360–367.

9. Cf. *ibid.*, pp. 359–360.

10. Cf. Reichenbach, *op. cit.*, sec. 27.

11. Cf. H. Törnebohm, *Concepts and Principles in the Space-Time Theory Within Einstein's Special Theory of Relativity* (Gothenburg: Almquist & Wiksell, 1963); H. Bondi, *Relativity and Common Sense* (New York: Doubleday, 1964), pp. 117–118; Bohm, *op. cit.*, Chap. XXVI; P. Suppes, "Axioms for Relativistic Kinematics With or Without Parity," in L. Henkin *et al,* eds., *The Axiomatic Method* (Amsterdam: North-Holland, 1959).

12. The ratio $t'/(t - d)$ is denoted as $k(v)$ by Bondi; hence, Bohm's term "K-calculus." Törnebohm calls it the "signal-connector."

13. H. Minkowski, "Space and Time," in J. J. C. Smart, ed., *Problems of Space and Time* (New York: Macmillan, 1964); see also J. J. C. Smart, *Between Science and Philosophy* (New York: Random House, 1968), pp. 218–236.

Chapter VI   The Causal Theory of Time and Space-Time

1. Cf. A. Grünbaum, *Philosophical Problems of Space and Time* (New York: Knopf, 1963), Chap. 15.

2. H. Reichenbach, *Modern Philosophy of Science* (London: Routledge and Kegan Paul, 1959), Chap. II.

3. R. Carnap, *Abriss der Logistik* (Vienna: Springer, 1929).

4. H. Reichenbach, *Axiomatik der relativistischen Raum-Zeit-Lehre* (Braunschweig: Vieweg, 1924).

5. H. Reichenbach, *The Philosophy of Space and Time* (New York: Dover, 1958), p. 136.

6. Cf. Reichenbach, *Axiomatik, op. cit.*, p. 22.

7. Reichenbach, *The Philosophy of Space and Time, op. cit.*, p. 136 (italics his).

8. H. Mehlberg, "Essai sur la théorie causale du temps," *Studia Philosophica,* I (1935), pp. 213–216; Grünbaum, *op cit.*, pp. 180–185.

9. Grünbaum, *op. cit.*, pp. 193–197.

10. *Ibid.*, pp. 196–197.

11. A. Grünbaum, *Modern Science and Zeno's Paradoxes* (Middletown: Wesleyan University Press, 1967), Chap. II, sec. 2C, pp. 56–64, presents the second formulation, for the case of open time. The complete formulation was presented by Dr. Grünbaum in his lectures in 1965; cf. B. C. van Fraassen, "Foundations of the Causal Theory of Time" (unpublished Ph.D. dissertation, University of Pittsburgh, 1966), Chap. I, sec. H2.

12. The account in this section bears certain similarities to Mehlberg's theory; cf. Mehlberg, *op. cit.;* van Fraassen, *op. cit.,* Chap. I, sec. F; and H. Mehlberg's recent articles "Space, Time, and Relativity," in Y. Bar-Hillel, ed., *Logic, Methodology, and Philosophy of Science* (Amsterdam: North-Holland, 1965), and "Relativity and the Atom," in P. K. Feyerabend and G. Maxwell, eds., *Mind, Matter and Method: Essays in Philosophy and Science in Honor of Herbert Feigl* (Minneapolis: University of Minnesota Press, 1966).

13. This paragraph is addressed to a difficulty raised by my student Philip Kuekes.

14. E. A. Milne claims that this is so; cf. Milne, *Kinematic Relativity* (Oxford, Eng.: Oxford University Press, 1948), and G. J. Whitrow, *The Structure and Evolution of the Universe* (New York: Harper & Row, 1959), pp. 129–135.

15. Cf. D. Bohm, *The Special Theory of Relativity* (New York: W. A. Benjamin, 1965), p. 26, and Reichenbach, *The Philosophy of Space and Time, op cit.*, secs. 17–18.

16. For a rigorous development of the theory of space-time of special relativity, cf. H. Törnebohm, *Concepts and Principles in the Space-Time Theory Within Einstein's Special Theory of Relativity* (Gothenburg: Almquist & Wiksell, 1963).

17. Cf. B. Russell, "On Order in Time," *Proceedings of the Cambridge Philosophical Society,* 32 (May, 1936), 216–228.

18. A fuller discussion of the problems of the "direct" approach is found in van Fraassen, *op. cit.,* Chap. III, sec. B.1.

19. *Ibid.,* Chap. III, sec. C; Chap. IV, sec. C.   The theory presented by Carnap, *op. cit.,* Pt. II, Chaps. D, G, appears to involve such a strong empirical postulate.

20. W. V. O. Quine, *Word and Object* (Cambridge, Mass.: M. I. T. Press, 1960), p. 225.

21. For a similar conceptualist position on the physical and logical modalities (in a sense that does not include counterfactuals), see B. C. van Fraassen, "Meaning Relations and Modalities" *Nous* 3 (1969), pp. 155–167.

Index

Index of Titles

ABOUT THE AUTHOR

BAS C. VAN FRAASSEN was born in the Netherlands and earned his B.A. from the University of Alberta. Both his M.A. and Ph.D. were granted by the University of Pittsburgh, where he studied with Adolf Grünbaum, the outstanding authority in the field of space and time philosophy. He has previously taught at Yale University and Indiana University and is currently Associate Professor of Philosophy at the University of Toronto. Among his honors are a National Science Foundation Grant and a John Simon Guggenheim Memorial Fellowship. Professor van Fraassen has also contributed to such journals as *Philosophy of Science, Zeitschrift für Mathematische Logik und Grundlagen der Mathematik,* and *Review of Metaphysics.*